КРИСТАЛЛОХИМИЯ
ПРОСТЕЙШИХ СОЕДИНЕНИЙ
УРАНА, ТОРИЯ,
ПЛУТОНИЯ И НЕПТУНИЯ

*Kristallokhimiya Prosteishikh Soedinenii
Urana, Toriya, Plutoniya i Neptuniya*

CRYSTAL CHEMISTRY of SIMPLE
COMPOUNDS of URANIUM, THORIUM,
PLUTONIUM, and NEPTUNIUM

CRYSTAL CHEMISTRY of SIMPLE COMPOUNDS
of Uranium, Thorium Plutonium, Neptunium

E. S. Makarov

TRANSLATED FROM RUSSIAN
by E. B. Uvarov, B.Sc., A.R.C.S., D.I.C., A.R.I.C.

QD
172
A3
M313

CONSULTANTS BUREAU, INC., NEW YORK

CHAPMAN & HALL, LTD., LONDON

1959

OHIO UNIVERSITY LIBRARY

The book contains exhaustive data on the crystal chemistry of the actinide elements. The arrangements of atoms in crystals of actinides and their simplest compounds, chiefly of thorium, uranium, plutonium, and neptunium, are considered. Certain crystal structure relationships are presented, concerned with the analogy between the actinides and the lanthanides and elements of the IVa, Va, and VIa subgroups of D. I. Mendeleev's periodic system.

Chief Editor: Academician A. P. Vinogradov

The original Russian text, from the V. I. Vernadskii Institute of Geochemistry and Analytical Chemistry, was published by the Academy of Sciences USSR Press in 1958.

Library of Congress Catalog Card Number: 59-14486

Copyright 1959 by Consultants Bureau, Inc.
227 W. 17th St., New York 11, N. Y.

All rights reserved. No part of this publication may be reproduced in any form without written permission from the publisher.

Printed in the United States of America

TABLE OF CONTENTS

Editorial Foreword		3
I.	Introduction	5
II.	Certain Questions of General Crystal Chemistry	6
	Classes of crystal structure	7
	Bond types and characteristics	8
	Molecular concepts in crystal chemistry	13
	Crystal-chemical groups of metallic compounds	15
III.	Crystal Structure of Polymorphic Modifications of Thorium, Uranium, Neptunium and Plutonium	27
	Thorium	
	1. α Th	28
	2. β Th	28
	Uranium	
	1. α U	29
	2. β U	30
	3. γ U	34
	Neptunium	
	1. α Np	34
	2. β Np	36
	3. γ Np	38
	Plutonium	
	1. α Pu	38
	2. β Pu	39
	3. γ Pu	39
	4. δ Pu	40
	5. δ' Pu	41
	6. ε Pu	41
	Other actinide elements	41

IV. Crystal Structure of Simple Compounds of Uranium,
   Thorium, Plutonium and Neptunium 42
      Subgroups Ia, IIa, IIIa 45
      Subgroups IVa, Va, VIa 45
      Subgroups VIIa, VIII 52
         1. Th_6Mn_{23} type 58
         2. $ThMn_{12}$ type 59
         3. Th_7Ni_3 type 60
         4. $ThCo$ type 61
         5. $ThNi$ type 63
         6. Th_2Ni_{17} type 64
         7. Th_2Fe_{17} type 66
         8. U_6Mn type 66
         9. UCo type 68
      Subgroup Ib 71
      Subgroup IIb 73
         1. Th_2Zn_{17} type 73
         2. U_2Zn_{17} type 74
      Subgroup IIIb 78
         1. UB_4 type 78
         2. UB_{12} type 80
         3. $ThAl$ type 82
         4. UGa type 83
         5. UAl_4 type 84
         6. $PuAl_3$ type 86
      Subgroup IVb 87
         1. U_3Si_2 type 88
         2. U_3Si type 90
         3. Pu_2C_3 type 92
         4. ThC_2 type 93
      Subgroups Vb, VIb 94
         1. Th_7S_{12} type 99
         2. $\alpha\ UO_3$ type 101
      Hydrogen and Subgroup VIIb 102
         1. ThH_2 (ThD_2) type 102
         2. Th_4H_{15} type 104
         3. $\beta\ UH_3$ (UD_3) type 106
         4. U_2F_9 type 107
         5. $\alpha\ UF_5$ type 109
         6. $\beta\ UF_5$ type 110

	7. UCl_3 type	111
	8. UCl_4 type	112
	9. UCl_6 type	113
	10. $PuBr_3$ type	114
V.	Atomic Radii of Actinides in Crystals	118
	Ionic radii of the actinides	119
	Covalent radii of the actinides...............	120
	Metallic radii of the actinides	122
VI.	Duality of the Chemical Nature of Thorium, Uranium, Neptunium and Plutonium.............	123
	Preliminary concepts	123
	The 5f elements	125
	1. The "Actinide" hypothesis	125
	2. The "Thoride" hypothesis	128
	3. The "5f Contraction".................	129
	Similarity of the 5f elements to the elements of subgroups IVa, Va and VIa	130
Literature Cited		141

EDITORIAL FOREWORD

E. S. Makarov's book, "Crystal Chemistry of Simple Compounds of Uranium, Thorium, Plutonium, and Neptunium," represents the first attempt to correlate crystal structure data on the simplest compounds of the most thoroughly studied actinide elements. No books dealing specifically with crystal chemistry of the actinides have been published hitherto either abroad or in the Soviet Union, although separate surveys by W. Zachariasen have appeared in various collective volumes.

There is no need to stress the great scientific and practical importance of studies of all aspects of the actinides and their compounds, including their crystal chemistry. The growing uses of atomic energy for peaceful purposes demand a deeper scientific understanding of the nature of the actinides. Such understanding must assist in the deliberate control of all the complex processes of nuclear power technology.

The abundant factual data on crystal structures of actinide compounds, summarized in this book in compact form, will enable research workers and engineers to make wider use of crystal structure data. Until now such data have been scattered over numerous literature sources.

Certain questions of general crystal chemistry are considered in Chapter II.

Chapters III—V give very full details of the crystal structures of the polymorphic modifications of the actinides and their simplest compounds; the ionic and atomic radii are also given.

The VIth and last chapter contains certain generalizations.

Since the discovery of neptunium and subsequently of all the other transuranic elements there has been continuing controversy as to which chemical element in the actinium–californium series is the parent of the "5f" family of elements. The "actinide" and the "uranide" hypotheses both have their supporters. The author has correctly adopted Seaborg's cautious position, preferring at the present time to speak not of "5f" elements as such, but of elements of the "5f–6d region."

Further, in our opinion the thesis advanced in the book concerning the dual chemical nature of the actinides, which are analogous both to the lanthanides and to elements of the IVa, Va, and VIa subgroups, is also of interest. It seems that the time is already ripe for stressing this duality of the actinides, in order to reveal more clearly the similarities and differences between the chemical behavior of these and other elements and to clarify their position in the Mendeleev periodic system.

КРИСТАЛЛОХИМИЯ
ПРОСТЕЙШИХ СОЕДИНЕНИЙ
УРАНА, ТОРИЯ,
ПЛУТОНИЯ И НЕПТУНИЯ

*Kristallokhimiya Prosteishikh Soedinenii
Urana, Toriya, Plutoniya i Neptuniya*

CRYSTAL CHEMISTRY of SIMPLE
COMPOUNDS of URANIUM, THORIUM,
PLUTONIUM, and NEPTUNIUM

I. INTRODUCTION

The scientific literature lacks adequately detailed reviews of the crystal chemistry of the compounds of the actinide elements. W. Zachariasen's article [1] reviews research on crystal chemistry mainly of compounds of the actinide elements or, as he calls them, the "5f elements," with nonmetals. There have also been many publications on the crystal structures of metallic compounds of thorium, uranium, plutonium, and to some extent of neptunium; therefore an attempt can now be made to elucidate the principal features of the crystal structure of the compounds formed by the actinide metals with all the elements of Mendeleev's periodic system, with retention of the classification by subgroups of the elements.

Such an attempt is made in this book; it is largely based on literature data published up to June, 1957.

At the present experimental stage in the development of crystal chemistry, this task reduces to an examination of the results obtained in determinations of atomic configurations, with subsequent elucidation of the nature of the atomic coordination and determinations of interatomic distances in crystals of metallic compounds of thorium, uranium, plutonium, and in part of neptunium.

II. CERTAIN QUESTIONS OF GENERAL CRYSTAL CHEMISTRY

Crystal chemistry can now be defined as the science of chemical structure of molecules in crystals--chemical structure in the sense understood by A. M. Butlerov and Kelkulé when they developed the theory of the chemical structure of organic molecules, with data on the chemical composition and certain chemical and physical properties of the compounds as the sole experimental material. Modern chemistry has at its disposal accurate information, not only on the nature and quantitative proportions of the atoms present in particular compounds, but also on the spatial arrangement of the atoms in the crystal lattices of the compounds. Experimental methods of crystal chemistry—x-ray diffraction, electron diffraction, and neutron diffraction--reveal the geometrical structure of crystals of chemical compounds. In many cases the geometry of atomic crystal structure leads to definite conclusions concerning the chemical structure of compounds, in the sense of their molecular structure and the correlation between the observed interatomic bonds and the valences of the atoms in the compound. This is true for most organic compounds. In the case of most inorganic compounds chemical crystallographers cannot as yet establish direct quantitative relationships between the experimentally observed geometry of the atomic structures and the effective valences of the atoms in these structures. This is a task for the future. Hence it is inevitable that at its present stage of development crystal chemistry is mainly concerned with spatial distribution of atoms in molecules and crystals.

There is no doubt that a complete quantitative theory of the chemical structure of molecules in crystals demands not only a knowledge of their geometrical structure but also evaluation of the interatomic bond energies. Development of the energy aspects of crystal chemistry is a task for thermodynamics and the electronic theory of solids, and is at its initial stage at the present time.

CLASSES OF CRYSTAL STRUCTURES

The entire range of crystal structures of elements and compounds can be subdivided into five classes according to the spatial relationships of the atoms: 1) molecular structures; 2) chain structures; 3) layer structures; 4) coordination structures; 5) mixed structures.

In the crystal lattice of a *molecular structure* the individual molecules (groups of atoms) of a given substance exist as more or less spatially-individualized structural units of a configuration determined by the nature of the atomic arrangement within the molecule. The interatomic distances within a given molecule are smaller than the corresponding interatomic distances for two neighboring molecules in a crystal.

In the crystal lattice of a *chain structure* the atoms are in the form of more or less separate chains, linear, spiral, or zigzag in form, extended in a definite direction for the given structure, and in principle of infinite length.

The interatomic distances within a given chain are shorter than the corresponding distances within the limits of two neighboring chains in a crystal. The atomic chains may be simple (unbranched) or branched.

In the crystal lattice of a *layer structure* the atoms are arranged in plane or puckered parallel sheets (packets), consisting of 1,2,3. . . . . sublayers, and in principle of infinite extension in the plane. The interatomic distances within a given layer are shorter than the corresponding distances within the limits of two neighboring atomic layers in a crystal. This means that the individual atomic sheets (packets) in a crystal are separated by "gaps" of free space.

In the crystal lattice of a *coordination structure* atomic formations (molecules, chains, layers) individualized in space cannot be distinguished, since each atom of a particular structural type has the same character of encirclement (coordination) by neighboring atoms, with equal interatomic distances from neighboring atoms of a given kind. In a coordination lattice all the atoms form a continuous spatial structure of a particular pattern, in principle of infinite extent (in practice limited by the dimensions of a single crystal).

The crystal lattice of a *mixed structure* may simultaneously contain different atomic arrangements, characteristic of the above classes of molecular, chain, layer, and coordination structures.

BOND TYPES AND CHARACTERISTICS

With a knowledge of interatomic distances and atomic coordination it is possible to deduce the nature of the bonds between particular atoms in crystals. On the other hand, the coordination number and the form of the coordination polyhedron for a given atom in a crystal may directly correspond to the number of its bonds and their direction in space; for example, this is the case of the carbon atom in the diamond. In general, however, there is no such direct correspondence, as the distribution of interatomic bond forces in space may be of a nondirected, spherically symmetrical character.

According to modern crystal chemistry, there are four principal types of interatomic bonds in solids: ionic, covalent, metallic, and van der Waals bonds.

For purpose of the subsequent discussion, the structural and physicochemical characteristics of each of these bond types are given below.

An ionic bond arises as the result of electrostatic attraction between ions of opposite charge, such as Na and Cl⁻ in NaCl. The characteristic feature of ionic compounds is that they crystallize with a coordination and not a molecular type of lattice. This suggests that the ionic bond is not directed in space, and has spherically symmetrical distribution. In principle this should lead to highly coordinated densely packed structures. In practice, however, this principle is restricted by two factors: first, by the strict relative proportions of cations and anions, necessary for balancing of the electrical charges; second, by definite limits of the ratio between the atomic radii of the anions and cations, which determines the stability of a given type of coordination. However, for given relationships between these factors, characteristic ionic compounds always crystallize in the most symmetrical and close-packed structures. Characteristic physicochemical properties of ionic compounds are ionic conductance in the fused state and nonconductance in the solid state, and solubility in appropriate solvents, with dissociation into ions.

A covalent or, more correctly, a nonpolar bond, exists between two chemically similar atoms sharing one, two, three, or four pairs of their valence electrons to form a stable electron configuration of the corresponding inert gas. In contrast to the ionic bond, the covalent bond has spatial direction, which predetermines the structural class. Thus, the existence of one bond formed by a pair of shared electrons between two atoms, as in H_2, or in Cl_2 and other halogens, leads to the formation of molecular structures. If an atom has two such shared electron pairs, this may lead either to the formation of a diatomic molecule (such as O_2), or to the formation of chains, which may either be closed into ring molecules containing a definite number of atoms (such as S_8), or they may be infinite (such as Se_∞). Accordingly, crystalline structures may belong to either the molecular or to the chain class. The presence of three covalent bonds may lead to the formation of sheet structures (for example, As_∞, Sb_∞, Bi_∞) in addition to molecular and chain structures. Finally, the presence of four covalent bonds, as in carbon atoms, leads to a three-dimensional bond distribution with formation, in general, of crystal structures of the coordination type (such as the diamond). The strict spatial localization of covalent bonds, when their number for a given atom is small, therefore leads to low coordination numbers of the atoms in covalent crystal structures, with relatively loose packing.

Characteristic physical properties of covalent compounds are: absence of electrical conductivity in the fused state, and insolubility in water.

Metallic bonds hold atoms in metals and alloys together by attraction between the positively charged atoms occupying the lattice points on the one hand, and the system of valence electrons constituting the mobile "electron gas," permeating the interatomic space of the crystal, on the other. This type of bonding does not place any spatial or quantitative limitations on typical metallic structures: the bonding of each atom in such a structure is distributed spherically in space among as many neighboring atoms as can be packed geometrically around the given atom. Therefore typical metals and their alloys assume coordination structures of the maximum close packing on crystallization.

Characteristic physical properties of substances with metallic bonds are: metallic luster, high electrical and thermal conductivity, and malleability.

Van der Waals bonds appear in purest form in the liquefaction and crystallization of the inert gases. Their physical nature is not fully understood, but in the structural sense they are analogous to metallic bonds, although immeasurably weaker than the latter, as shown by the low melting points of solid inert gases and of typical saturated molecular compounds. Van der Waals bonds are not spatially directed; this leads to maximum close packing in the structure of solid inert gases, and to relatively close packing of saturated molecules in molecular crystals.

It follows from this brief account of the four types of interatomic bonds that in general there is no direct connection between a given bond type and a definite class of structure, and that if two or more substances have a crystal structure of the same type this does not necessarily indicate that the type of bonding in them is the same. It is only in conjunction with characteristic physical and chemical properties that crystal structure data can help to decide the nature of the type of bonding in a given substance.

The next important principle of general crystal chemistry is the possibility of continuous transition between different types of bonding. Essentially, all the infinite variety of real crystalline phases of constant and variable composition constitutes a kind of *continuum of transitional states* between the four limiting bond types: covalent, ionic, metallic, and the van der Waals type. The tendency of interacting atoms to assume, in one way or another, the stable electron configuration of an atom of the corresponding inert gas is a common feature of ionic, covalent, and metallic bonds. This makes continuous transition between these types of bonding possible. In crystals with ionic bonding the valence electrons are completely localized in the atomic orbits of the anions, and therefore the negative charge (electron density) is distributed periodically, roughly speaking, at lattice *points*. In covalent crystals the valence electrons of the nearest neighbor atoms are shared, forming strictly directed *linear* bonds or "bridges" of higher electron density. In metallic crystals the valence electrons of all the atoms collectively form an electron gas (cloud) which is distributed uniformly over the entire free *volume* of the interionic lattice space.

It is clear that any transitional state is possible between *point*, *linear*, and *volume* distribution of electron density in crystals, owing to "spreading" or "tightening" of electron density. This forms the basis of the above-mentioned concept of the continuum of transitional bond states. (It is assumed that the van der Waals bonding component is always present to some degree in conjunction with any other type of bonding.) This viewpoint accounts for the existence of a class of mixed structures, in which the structural and physical characteristics of ionic, covalent, and metallic bonding may be interwoven. It is because of the widespread occurrence of mixed structures that the real world of crystalline phases does not contain absolutely pure representatives of ionic, covalent, metallic, or van der Waals bonding. One can only speak of representatives of these four types of bonding which more or less approximate to ideality. Even in molecules of organic compounds certain bond electrons may be delocalized and have a "metallic" character.

The distribution of electron density in crystals has been studied experimentally by the methods of x-ray Fourier synthesis, and the scanty data so far available fully confirm the above qualitative picture of four bonding types and their simultaneous presence in mixed structures.

It must be pointed out that despite the clarity of the qualitative picture of bonding, there is as yet no strict unified physical theory which could be used for quantitative description of bond forces and their nature in all the diversity of crystal structures, although considerable theoretical successes have been achieved in the solution of many specific crystal-chemical problems.

The four principal types of interatomic bonding in crystals described above, augmented by the concept of the continuum of transitional bond states, provide a qualitative description of all the diversity of solid phases, both from the physical and from the chemical standpoints. In general there are no sound reasons for making any significant distinction between these standpoints, as they originated separately for historical reasons rather than in principle, because of the distinction in the nature of physical and chemical forces of interatomic bonding. In practice, however, both physicists and chemists often distinguish between concepts of *physical* forces of atomic cohesion in crystals and *chemical* valence forces of interatomic bonding.

Crystal chemistry shows that in general a sharp line cannot be drawn between "physical" and "chemical" interatomic bonds in crystals, as they are unified. The existence of chemical bonds between atoms always leads to greater physical cohesion. It is well known that interatomic bonding is weak in crystals of the inert gases (A, Ne, Kr, Xe), indicated by their extremely low melting points and explained by the absence of covalent bonds between the atoms and the presence of only very weak van der Waals forces of interatomic attraction. In just the same way crystals composed of chemically saturated nonpolar molecules have low melting or sublimation points and low hardness, since the individual molecules, although firmly bound internally by chemical bond forces, are interconnected by only very weak van der Waals forces (examples are O_2, CO_2, Cl_2, organic compounds). The existence of polar, hydrogen, or hydroxyl bonds between molecules of organic or inorganic compounds considerably increases the thermal stability and physical strength of crystals of these compounds in comparison with crystals of nonpolar compounds (such as ice or high polymers). The strength of interatomic cohesion is even greater in ionic and especially in covalent coordination crystals, where the chemical bond forces are not enclosed within the limits of spatially restricted molecules but permeate the entire crystal as one giant molecule (for example, NaCl, SiC, diamond). The diamond is a particularly vivid example of the unity of physical and chemical bonding in crystals: being *physically* the strongest (hardest, infusible) solid, the diamond crystal consists of an aggregation of carbon atoms interconnected by purely *chemical* covalent bonds.

The chemical bond, in the widest sense, should be taken to mean an interatomic bond such that the bound atoms acquire, in one manner or another, the most stable electronic configurations for the given physicochemical conditions (temperature, pressure, chemical composition), as the result of which the system assumes the energy state which is the most advantageous under the same conditions. From this point of view chemical bonding must include not only ionic and covalent bonding, but also metallic bonding, characterized by the presence of cations with the electron configuration on inert gas atoms in the crystal, and an electron gas permeating the cation lattice; the electron gas here acts as a "collective anion" if metals are compared with ionic compounds.

MOLECULAR CONCEPTS IN CRYSTAL CHEMISTRY

Even the earliest determinations, performed during the initial development of crystal chemistry, of the structures of such well-known typical chemical compounds as NaCl, ZnS, CaF_2, SiO_2, Cu_2O, $CaCO_3$, etc., revealed the absence of individualized molecular groupings in the crystals of these substances.

However, it was found in other cases, such as solid carbon dioxide and all organic compounds, that certain crystals have a molecular structure. Most recent work has shown that as a rule crystals or organic compounds have a molecular structure, but that the vast majority of inorganic crystals do not contain finite molecular groups.

The absence of discrete molecules in the crystals of such typical chemical compounds as the above-mentioned NaCl, SiO_2, $CaCO_3$, etc., still remains difficult to understand by many chemists who are afraid to change their accustomed molecular concepts, developed from the time of Avogadro and Cannizzaro for the chemistry of gases and liquids.

It is clear that before the existence of x-ray structural analysis there was no direct way of determining the arrangements of atoms in solids, and chemists were forced to extend their concepts of the structure of gases and liquids to the structure of solids, or to study solids experimentally in solution or in the vapor state, which, of course, is not equivalent to studying the solid state. Chemists often, without adequate justification, assumed the atomic proportions of the components of solid compounds, determined by chemical analysis, to be equal to the numbers of atoms in the molecules of these compounds. For example, if chemical analysis gave an atomic composition represented by the empirical formula of the type AB_2, this formula was automatically promoted to the status of a molecule and it was assumed that the compound consisted of discrete AB_2 molecules. Whereas this procedure was completely justified for gaseous compounds, in which discrete molecules have real existence, and to some extent justified for certain simplest liquid compounds, the nature of the solid state was too complex for these primitive concepts.

It should not be thought that there are any fundamental contradictions between crystal chemistry and the old classical chemistry. Crystal chemistry is an integral part of modern general chemistry, and its results augment, reinterpret, and in some cases solve problems associated with the solid state of matter. Therefore there can be no doubt that in such questions as the inner structure of crystals crystal chemistry has the final say.

How does crystal chemistry account for the seeming disappearance of molecules in crystals of solid chemical compounds? Many crystal chemists and physicists consider that molecules in inorganic compounds do not disappear but, on the contrary, attain such gigantic dimensions that they can be held in the hand as individual *single crystals* of compounds such as NaCl, ZnS, SiO_2, $CaCO_3$, etc.

In the case of many solid inorganic compounds the concept of discrete micromolecules should be replaced by the concept of giant continuous macromolecules which extend, indefinitely in principle, in three, two, or one dimension of the crystal lattice space, corresponding to the coordination, layer, and chain types of structure respectively.

This concept is not new, as processes of polymerization and the formation of giant chain molecules--macromolecules--have long been known in organic chemistry in relation to such substances as cellulose, rubber, fibrous proteins, high polymers, etc. In inorganic chemistry the world of giant molecules is much more extensively and diversely represented, because of the greater number of chemical elements and bond types within the scope of inorganic chemistry. In inorganic crystal chemistry too we find different intermediate steps between discrete micromolecules and giant molecules, as the result of polymerization (for example, the formation of dimers of Al_2Cl_6, Fe_2Cl_6).

It should be pointed out that the concept of a "molecule" in the coordination, layer, and chain types of structure cannot be regarded as finally settled at the present time.

CRYSTAL-CHEMICAL GROUPS OF METALLIC COMPOUNDS

Whereas the behavior of metals with nonmetals has been studied fairly fully and adequately, this cannot be said of the behavior of metals with each other. The science of metallic alloys began to develop within the framework of a technical discipline--metallography--rather than within the framework of inorganic chemistry.

In the chemistry of metallic alloys we consider chemical compounds, known as metallic or intermetallic compounds, and also solid and liquid solutions of metals in each other. Characteristic features of intermetallic compounds are that they do not conform to stoichiometric or ordinary valence rules, and that the laws of constant composition and multiple proportions often break down. The chief task of the chemistry of metallic alloys, not yet accomplished, is to find the laws of formation of intermetallic phases and to explain them theoretically. Crystal chemistry has an important role to play in the solution of this problem.

Intermetallic compounds show a great diversity of crystal structures and physicochemical properties. No general law covering the whole range of intermetallic phases has yet been discovered for the crystal chemistry of metallic alloys. The Hume-Rothery rule was considered for a long time to be such a law, but it proved valid only for a definite group of alloys of the brass type, and certainly does not cover the whole range of intermetallic phases.

In reality, intermetallic phases can, in our present state of knowledge, be subdivided into several large *chrystal-chemical groups,* each of which conforms to its own empirically determined laws, which confer to each group its specific characteristics. A list of these groups is given below, pure metals being taken as the first group; the subsequent groups are given in order of decreasing metallic properties and increasing nonmetallic properties, in accordance with the structural and physicochemical characteristics of the different types of bonding:

1. Metals
   a) typical
   b) semimetals

2. Disordered solid solutions of metals

3. Ordered phases

4. Close-packed intermetallic phases

5. Phases of the brass type

6. Phases of the LiAl and NaTl type

7. Phases of the nickel arsenide type

8. Phases of the Mg_2Sn and $AuAl_2$ type

9. Normal-valence intermetallic phases.

The characteristic crystal-chemical feature of *typical* metals is formation of structures with close packing of atoms in the crystals as follows:

Each atom has:

1. Hexagonal close packing ⎫
2. Cubic close packing ⎬ 12 nearest equidistant neighbors

3. Cubic body-centered packing ⎫ 8 nearest and 6 near neighbors

The formation of close-packed structures in metals is accounted for by the nondirected, spherical nature of the force field in metallic bonding.

The behavior of *semimetals* is quite different. The characteristic crystal-chemical feature of the semimetals is the formation of (8–N) structures, i.e., structures in which each atom has (8–N) nearest neighbors (where N is the number of the group of the periodic system to which the metal belongs), and not 12 neighbors as in the typical metals. It is postulated in crystal chemistry that the formation of (8–N) structures is due to the presence of (8–N) covalent, spatially directed bonds for each atom of this group, superposed on the metallic bond. The gradual increase of metallic properties with increase of the number of covalent bonds, and gradual transition of the latter into metallic bonding is illustrated especially clearly by the following series of crystals:

No. of b subgroups →	VII	VI	V	IV	III	II	I
Element →	Br	Se	As	Ge	Ga	Zn	Cu
(8–N) nearest neighbors in crystal	1	2	3	4	5	6	12

Many metals are miscible in all proportions either in the melted state or after solidification, forming continuous series of liquid and solid solutions (for example: Au–Cu, Fe–Cr, Mg–Cd, As–Sb, Se–Te).

Continuous binary solid solutions may be stable over definite temperature ranges, and often pass into ordered phases below a certain temperature.

Continuous solid solutions are formed when the alloying metals are closely similar in bonding type and atomic size; similarity of lattice symmetry between the components is favorable, but in general not obligatory. Two cases of solid-solution formation are distinguished:

1) solid solutions without changes of lattice symmetry on change of chemical composition (for example, Cu—Au);

2) solid solutions with changes of symmetry as the composition varies (for example, Cu—γMn).

A characteristic crystal-chemical feature of *continuous solid solutions* of metals is retention of the crystal structure of the components, with atoms of both kinds randomly distributed over the lattice sites. In the lattice of a disordered solid solution the atoms of the components are similar in size and chemical nature. The total coordination number in the lattice of a solid solution remains the same as in the lattices of the original components. The interatomic distances in solid solutions are generally intermediate between those for the components, but usually the relationship is not linear, but with deviations; either contraction (more frequently) or expansion (rarely). These results suggest that the nature of bonding in continuous disordered solid solutions does not differ greatly from that in the original components. For instance, if in the typical metals Au and Ag the bonding is purely metallic, it remains of the same type in solid Au—Ag solutions; if in Bi and Sb the bonding is not purely metallic, but is superposed with covalent bonding, the bonding in solid Bi—Sb solutions is covalent—metallic. The existence of "short-range order" in the lattice of solid solutions of this type indicates a tendency to transition into a state characteristic of "ordered phases."

In the great majority of cases in binary intermetallic systems we find *limited solubility* of one metal in the other. In the phase diagrams the regions of solid solutions adjacent to the pure components are usually described as α solid solutions.

The atoms of a dissolved element can be distributed in the lattice of the solvent metal either by substitution or interstitially; in either case the lattice symmetry of the solvent metal may vary continuously, or it may not. Accordingly, four principal structural types of α-solid solutions may be distinguished:

a) substitutional α solid solutions without change of lattice symmetry, such as α (Ag—Mg);

b) substitutional α solid solutions with change of lattice symmetry, such as α (In—Tl);

c) interstitial α solid solutions without change of lattice symmetry, such as α (αTi—O);

d) interstitial α solid solutions with change of lattice symmetry, such as α (V—O).

In contrast to continuous solid solutions, limited α solid solutions can, as we have seen, be either substitutional or interstitial, and may include combinations of elements very different in the chemical sense, and therefore in the type of bonding. Therefore the character of bonding in α solid solutions may in general vary over wider limits than in continuous solid solutions, and it may involve considerable superposition of covalent and ionic bonding. In such cases α phases are regarded more correctly as chemical compounds of variable composition rather than "solid solutions." This is especially true for "interstitial phases," which include all α solid solutions of nonmetals in transition metals.

Disordered solid solutions, in which atoms of the components occupy the lattice sites statistically, may, below a certain critical temperature, pass into the ordered state, in which atoms of different kinds occupy relative positions in a certain repeating sequence in the lattice.

Ordered phases is the term we shall use for phases which have arisen as the result of ordering of disordered solid solutions, both of the continuous and the limited α type.

All the known and well-studied cases of ordered-phase formation belong to substitutional solid solutions. Ordered phases may form either without change of lattice symmetry in a disordered solid solution or, less frequently, with a change of the lattice symmetry of the disordered solid solution from which a particular ordered phase is formed. Real examples of ordered phases belong to three widely distributed types of metallic structures: cubic body-centered, cubic face-centered, and hexagonal close-packed.

The existing results of structure investigations show that no systems with continuous solid solutions of metals with cubic body-centered lattices are found to contain ordered phases with the type of order which is the simplest for this structure--the CsCl type. For example, in the systems Fe--Cr and Fe--V continuous solid solutions in the composition regions of FeCr and FeV decompose, below 900 and 1200° respectively, into regions of ordered tetragonal σ phases having a complex structure related to β U, of low symmetry and not yet finally established.

The following three types of ordered structures in solid solutions based on the cubic body-centered structure with two atoms in the unit cell are known:

a) FeAl
b) Fe_3Al
c) Cr_2Al

The following principal and well-studied types of superlattice for ordered phases based on cubic face-centered structure are known:

Cu_3Au
$CuAu_I$
CuPt
$CuPt^*_{2.64}$
$CuPt_7$
$CuAu_{II}$
CuPd

Two types of superlattice are known for ordered phases based on hexagonal close packing:

MgCd
Mg_3Cd (Ni_3Sn)

---
* Formerly known as $CuPt_3$.

In many metallic systems formation of continuous or extensive regions of solid solutions and ordered phases is not achieved because of the unfavorable volume ratios of the atoms or because of significant differences in the chemical nature of the atoms. In such systems intermediate intermetallic phases of constant or variable composition may be formed, and in general the composition of such a phase need not correspond to a simple ratio of the components. If the combining elements are of a pronounced metallic character, their compounds are also metallic; the primary effect of this is that under the influence of the force field, spherical in character, of the metallic bond the atoms are packed in the most compact manner in the crystal lattice of the compound. It is known that in close packing of *equal* spherical atoms, as in the true metals, the coordination number cannot exceed 12. In close packing of atoms of *different* size it is evident that the coordination number may be greater than 12, and that it depends on the ratio of the atomic radii and on the symmetry conditions of the structure in which the compound crystallizes.

In the group of *close-packed intermetallic phases* we include phases having highly coordinated crystal structures, i.e., such that the total coordination number of atoms of at least one kind is greater, or at least not less than 12. Although such structures are formed under the dominating influence of the metallic bond, many of them include indications of superposition of covalent bonding between like atoms, as shown by the formation of three-dimensional, plane, linear, or even "island" (discrete molecular) atomic groupings, clearly distinguishable in the general lattice by the nature of the coordination, or by a shortening of the interatomic distances in comparison with the sum of the atomic radii in the elemental state.

The group of close-packed intermetallic phases is not characterized by any special relationships except the most general one, namely that the components of these phases are well-defined metals, and that the types of their crystal structure are, so to speak, the privilege of the metallic state, since saltlike phases do not as a rule crystallize in such structures.

The commonest and most typical representatives of the group of close-packed intermetallic phases crystallize in the following structural types:

$MgCu_2$, $MgZn_2$, $MgNi_2$, $CaZn_5$, $PdBe_5$
$NaZn_{13}$
$CaPb_3$, $TiNi_3$
SiV_3 (βW)
AlB_2 $BiIn_2$
$CuAl_2$

Phases of the brass type are the β, γ and ε phases of the system copper--zinc, and many analogous phases formed by Cu, Ag, Au, and the transition metals on the one hand, and "semimetals" on the other. Since such phases as a rule correspond to definite "electron concentrations," measured by the ratio of the total number of valence electrons to the total number of atoms in the unit cell of the given phase, J. D. Bernal proposed in 1933 the term "electronic compounds" for such phases. The electron concentrations are:

for β phases: 3/2

for γ phases: 21/13

for ε phases: 7/4

These phases are also often known as "Hume-Rothery phases," after the British scientist who formulated the rules of electron concentration jointly with A. Westgren in 1926.

We have seen that in the group of close-packed intermetallic phases the "guiding" principle was solely the principle of close packing of the atoms or atomic groups, and the electron concentration did not conform to any definite law, such as in the case for phases of the brass type. In general, it seems unlikely that the electron concentration plays no role at all in the group of close-packed phases, as in the last analysis it determines the nature of the filling of the Brillouin energy zones which, in their turn, predetermine the crystal structure assumed by a given phase. It is possible that our ignorance of the effective numbers of valence (free) electrons in pure metals and their compounds prevents us from revealing the laws governing electron concentrations in the group of close-packed intermetallic phases. However, in the phases of the brass type, where heteropolarity apparently already plays a significant role, the normal metal valences become more important in atomic interaction, and this determines the relative stability of the 3/2, 21/13, and 7/4 electron concentrations in large groups of the β, γ and ε phases. It is true that even here it is necessary to make certain arbitrary assumptions in order to satisfy the electron-concentration rules; for example, the valence of the transition metals is generally taken as zero, but sometimes, as in β (Ni—Zn), γ (Cr—Al) the valences of Ni and Cr are assumed to be 1, and of Al, 2.

Thus, the guiding crystallographic principle in the group of phases of the brass type is the principle of characteristic 3/2, 21/13, and 7/4 electron concentrations. All phases of the brass type have extensive regions of homogeneous chemical composition and are typical compounds of variable composition.

If the alkali and earth metals instead of the elements of the copper subgroup or the transition elements are considered in conjunction with elements of the first and second b subgroups (Zn, Cd, Hg, Al, Ga, In, Tl), then in such systems we find phases of the composition AB, which are close in the structural sense to the β phases of the brass type. These include phases of the LiAl type, with a cubic structure of the CsCl type, and phases of the NaTl type, the structure of which is derived from the CsCl type. In the crystal-chemical sense, phases of the LiAl and NaTl types are characterized by the fact that in the main they do not conform to the 3/2 electron concentration typical for β phases of the brass type. The electron concentration for LiAl and NaTl is 4/2 = 2.

In alloys of the transition metals with semimetals of subgroup b and with certain nonmetals (sulfur, selenium), the so-called *nickel arsenide phases* are formed, having wide regions of homogeneous variable composition, ranging from A_2B to AB_2. In their crystal structure these phases are derived from the homologous Ni_2In—NiAs—$NiTe_2$, structure types or structures directly belonging to these types, for the compositions A_2B, AB, and AB_2 respectively.

In the crystal-chemical sense the group of nickel arsenide phases occupies an intermediate position between phases of the γ brass type, the structure of which is closely related to the Ni_2In type of structure, and phases of the $NiTe_2$ type, the layer structure of which, belonging to the CdI_2 type, is characteristic of the saltlike rather than of the metallic state. Consequently the character of interatomic bonding in nickel arsenide phases varies within wide limits from predominantly metallic to ionic--covalent.

Phases of the nickel arsenide type are allied by the nature of their coordination to phases of the Co_2Si, Rh_2Ge and Mn_5Si_3 types.

Phases of the Mg_2Sn and Al_2Au type are isomorphous; they have a cubic structure of the fluorite or the antifluorite type. The prefix "anti" implies that the anionic part of the lattice in CaF_2 is structurally equivalent to the cationic (magnesium) part of the lattice in Mg_2Sn, while the cationic part of the lattice in CaF_2 is structurally equivalent to the anionic (tin) part of the lattice in Mg_2Sn. The difference between phases of the Mg_2Sn and Al_2Au types is that whereas the former conform to the classical valence rules and can be formally described as "ionic compounds," the latter do not conform to these rules (at least, in explicit form). However, the conformity to the classical valence rules in phases of the Mg_2Sn type is only apparent, since the metallic properties (metallic luster, electronic conductance) of such phases do not indicate that they contain purely ionic bonds, when both the valence electrons of magnesium would completely pass to the Sn^{4-} anion. In reality, we do not yet know the effective valences of atoms in phases with metallic type of bonding, or else we do not know the hidden mechanisms of interatomic bonding whereby the classic valences of the atoms are manifested.

To speak figuratively, phases with the fluorite structure have "one foot" in the group of chemical compounds with normal valence, this foot being the group of phases of the Mg_2Sn type, while the "other foot" (Al_2Au) stands in the group of intermetallic phases, where nonconformity to the valence rules of chemistry is usual. The nature of interatomic bonding in compounds of the fluorite type varied over wide limits from ionic for typical salts, to essentially metallic for intermetallic compounds of the Al_2Au type.

The gradual transition from ionic to metallic bonding in fluorite phases can be illustrated by the following series of compounds:

$$Cl_2Sr - Cu_2S - Ir_2P - Mg_2Si - Al_2Au$$

$$F_2Ca - Na_2Te - (Cu, Mg)Sb - Mg_2Sn - In_2Pt$$

We shall give the name of *normal-valence phases* to intermetallic phases the composition of which conforms to the usual valences of their constituent elements, and which can be explained by the presence of ionic or covalent interatomic bonds. These phases are formed when semimetals combine with each other, or when alkali or alkaline-earth metals combine with semimetals, and they are close to ionic or covalent salts in the nature of their interatomic bonding, although they retain more or less pronounced metallic properties. All these phases have either vanishingly narrow regions of variable composition, or are of constant chemical composition, simple and rational in relation to the valence rules. Among a considerable variety of normal-valence intermetallic phases the following structural types are the most common:

MgSe (NaCl type), AlSb (ZnS_{cub} type), MgFe (ZnS_{hex} type),

Na_3As, Mg_3Bi_2 (La_2O_3 type), Mg_3As_2 (Mn_2O_3 type), Li_3Bi (BiF_3 type)

Apart from the phases included in the above groups, there are numerous smaller groups and single phases with individual structures, which either occupy intermediate positions between these groups, or approximate more or less closely to one of them. All the region of intermetallic phases as a whole is a continuum of transitional bond states between the metallic and salt classes of substances. The above crystal-chemical groups of intermetallic phases can be regarded as the main landmarks which can be distinguished at the present time in the course of such transitions. The type of bonding in each of these groups is not strictly limited, but allows of more or less wide variations in relative proportions of metallic, covalent, and ionic bonds. Gradual structural transitions, reflecting gradual changes of bond character, have already been found between certain crystal-chemical groups; for example, between the groups of phases of the γ brass and of the nickel arsenide types. In other cases, such as in the group of phases with the fluorite type of structure (phases of the Mg_2Sn--Al_2Au type), a gradual transition of bond type from saltlike to metallic may be observed within the limits of a single structural type. More detailed studies of the dependence of the crystal structure of intermetallic phases on their chemical composition will in the future lead to the discovery of new relationships between the different phase groups.

III. CRYSTAL STRUCTURE OF POLYMORPHIC MODIFICATIONS OF THORIUM, URANIUM, NEPTUNIUM, AND PLUTONIUM

Polymorphic modifications of a given element, or its allotropes, are different forms in which the atoms of the same element are joined to each other. The interatomic bonding in them is effected by electrons, and allotropes may be regarded as simple chemical compounds of the atoms of the given element with each other. They should form the starting point in consideration of the crystal chemistry of the compounds of each element.

The polymorphism of the actinides is very diverse and interesting. Its complexity in general increases in the transition from thorium to plutonium. Whereas thorium exists in only two modifications, with simple crystal structures of the usual metal type, uranium and neptunium each exist in three, and plutonium in six; nearly all the modifications of uranium, neptunium, and plutonium are unique and have no analogs among elements of lower atomic number. This is indicative of the peculiar nature of the electronic structure of the atoms of these heavy elements, and of the high sensitivity of the electronic states in these atoms to temperature changes, if it is taken into account that polymorphic changes of a substance are caused by changes in the electronic structures of the bound atoms and by corresponding qualitative changes in the interatomic bonds. Indeed, as will be shown later, in the case of plutonium there are five atomic rearrangements, associated with polymorphic transitions, in the temperature range from 122 to 476°.

The common feature of the polymorphism of the actinides under consideration is that the highest-temperature modifications (in the prefusion state) of thorium, uranium, neptunium, and plutonium all have the same crystal structure—a simple cubic body-centered structure of the α Fe type.

We now consider the atomic arrangements and interatomic distances individually for each modification of thorium, uranium, neptunium, and plutonium.

THORIUM

It was believed until 1954 that elemental thorium exists only in the cubic face-centered modification. In 1954 Chiotti [2] showed that at temperatures above 1400° a cubic body-centered modification of thorium is formed, stable up to the melting point of the metal. Therefore it is now considered that thorium exists in two modifications, the low-temperature modification, α Th, and the high-temperature modification, β Th.

1. α Th is stable at temperatures up to 1400°. Structure – cubic face-centered of the Cu type [1]. Cubic close packing with four atoms in the unit cell. Space group O_h^5 — Fm3m. Atomic coordinates: 000, $0\frac{1}{2}\frac{1}{2}$, $\frac{1}{2}0\frac{1}{2}$, $\frac{1}{2}\frac{1}{2}0$. Lattice constant a = 5.085A*. Each atom has twelve nearest neighbors at a distance of $\frac{\sqrt{2}}{2} \cdot a =$ 3.59 A, and hence the atomic radius of α Th is 1.795 A.

2. β Th is stable at temperatures above 1400°. Structure—cubic, body-centered of the α Fe type, with two atoms in the unit cell. Space group O_h^9 — Im3m. Atomic coordinates 000, $\frac{111}{222}$. Lattice constant a= 4.11 A. Each atom has eight nearest neighbors at a distance of $\frac{\sqrt{3}}{2} \cdot a =$ 3.56 A, and hence the atomic radius of β Th is 1.78 A.

---
*Here and subsequently the lattice constants and interatomic distances are given in true angstroms, 1 A = 1.002 kX..

URANIUM

1. αU is stable at temperatures up to 668° [3]. The crystal structure of αU was determined in 1937 by Jacob and Warren, by the powder method [4]. This structure was subsequently confirmed by Lukesh [5] on a single crystal of α U. The structure of αU is rhombic, of unique type. Lattice constants: a = 2.858 A; b = 5.877 A; c = 4.955 A. The unit cell contains four uranium atoms. Space group D_{2h}^{17} -- Cmcm. Atomic coordinates 4U in 4(c): $0 y \frac{1}{4}$; $\frac{1}{2}\frac{1}{2}+ + y\frac{1}{4}$; $0 \bar{y}\frac{3}{4}$; $\frac{1}{2}\frac{1}{2} - y\frac{3}{4}$; $y = 0.105$.

The structure of α U is a rhombically distorted hexagonal close-packed structure. A characteristic feature of the structure of αU is formation of zigzag chains of atoms running through the crystal in the direction of the z axis, as shown in the projection of the structure in Fig. 1. Each atom has two nearest neighbors at a

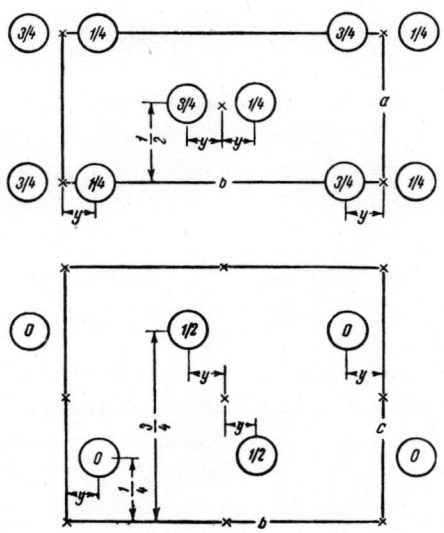

Fig. 1. Projection of the structure of αU on the cell face, after Jacob and Warren.

distance of 2.77 A in its zigzag chain. The two next nearest neighbors are in other chains at a distance of 2.86 A. In addition, there are four further neighbors at a distance of 3.28 A and four more at a distance of 3.37 A.

Thus the atomic radius of uranium, taken as one half of the nearest interatomic distance, is 1.385 A. The "metallic" atomic radius of uranium, i.e., corrected to coordination number 12, say by Pauling's method [6], is 1.53 A.

A very interesting property of αU, which has not yet received a full theoretical explanation, is the strong anisotropy of thermal expansion of αU, with a negative coefficient along the y axis [3].

2. βU is stable between 668 and 774° [3]. The structure is tetragonal of unique type. The values given by Tucker [7] and by Thewlis [8] for the lattice constants of uranium--chromium alloy and of pure βU differ somewhat, but Tucker himself pointed out [7] that the lattice constants given by Thewlis are more accurate.

The lattice constants are as follows. According to Thewlis [8], βU at 720° has: $a = 10.759 \pm 0.001$ A, $c = 5.656 \pm 0.001$ A; calculated density $\delta = 18.11$ g/cc; the characteristic Debye temperature is 270° K. Uranium alloyed with chromium (1.4 atomic %) quenched at 720° has the following constants (at room temperature): $a =$ $= 10.590 \pm 0.001$ A; $c = 5.634 \pm 0.001$ A; density $\delta = 18.56$ g/cc; according to Tucker [7]: $a = 10.52$ A; $c = 5.57$ A. The lattice constants of the same alloy at 720°: $a = 10.763 \pm 0.005$ A; $c = 5.652 \pm$ ± 0.005 A; calculated density 17.93 g/cc.

The crystal structure of βU was first determined by Tucker for a single crystal of uranium alloyed with chromium (1.4 atomic %) quenched at 720° [7]. Tucker found that in this case the structure of βU is very complex, and belongs to a noncentrosymmetrical group C_{4v}^4 – P4nm. Thewlis [8] studied the structure of a pure sample of βU by the powder method at high temperatures; his results in general confirmed Tucker's findings, but with some differences in the experimental intensities of the x-ray interferences.

Subsequently Tucker and Senio [9] used new values for the intensities of the interference lines to modify the structure originally proposed for βU, and referred it to the centrosymmetrical space group D_{4h}^{14} — P4/mnm. Finally, in 1954 Thewlis and Steeple [10] modified still further the atomic parameters of the βU structure within the framework of the noncentrosymmetrical space group C_{4V}^{14} — P4nm. The structure attributed by Thewlis and Steeple to βU occupies an intermediate position between the variants proposed by Tucker [7] and by Tucker and Senio [9] respectively, and may be regarded at the present time as the closest approximation to reality. The data of Thewlis and Steeple on the crystal structure of βU are given below.

The unit cell of βU contains 30 atoms. Space group C_{4V}^{4} — P4nm. Atomic coordinates*: $2U_I$ in 2(a) : z = 0.68; $4U_{II}$ in 4(c) : x = 0.105, z = 0.22; $4U_{III}$ in 4(c) : x = 0.290, z = 0.00 $\pm$ 0.02; $4U_{IV}$ in 4(c) : x = = 0.690, z = 0.48; $8U_V$ in 8(d) : x = 0.547, y = 0.227, z = 0.27; $8U_{VI}$ in 8(d) : x = 0.367, y = 0.041, z = 0.18.

The projection of the structure of βU onto the (001) plane is shown in Fig. 2. The atoms lie in puckered networks arranged in layers perpendicular to the four-fold axis at levels approximately corresponding to z = 0; 0.25; 0.50; 0.75. The atomic coordination is complex and difficult to represent visually. The numbers of neighboring atoms and the corresponding interatomic distances for all six kinds of βU atoms are given in Table 1.

The characteristic feature of the βU structure is formation of $U_V - U_{VI}$ diatomic molecules with a considerably shortened interatomic distance of 2.531 A, and of $U_{III} - U_{IV}$ molecules with a distance of 2.732 A. A section of the βU cell along the (110) plane is shown in Fig. 3, with $U_V - U_{VI}$ molecules indicated by dash lines.

---

* The significance of the coordinates is explained in [11]. The accuracy of the atomic parameters is discussed in the original paper by Thewlis and Steeple [10].

TABLE 1

INTERATOMIC DISTANCES IN βU

Atom	Number of neighbors	Interatomic distances, A	Atom	Number of neighbors	Interatomic distances, A
U_I	4	3.023	U_{IV}	1	3.352
	2	3.053		2	3.411
	4	3.353		1	3.447
	2	3.447		2	3.571
U_{II}	2	2.911	U_V	1	2.531
	1	3.053		1	2.831
	1	3.077		1	2.926
	2	3.182		1	2.951
	1	3.196		1	3.023
	2	3.447		1	3.071
	2	3.571		1	3.182
	2	3.651		1	3.231
	2	3.907		1	3.295
U_{III}	1	2.732		1	3.439
	2	2.926		1	3.487
	1	2.957		1	3.651
	2	2.983			
	1	3.077	U_{VI}	1	2.531
	2	3.231		1	2.831
	1	3.352		1	2.911
	2	3.664		1	2.983
	2	3.907		1	2.995
				1	3.071
U_{IV}	1	2.732		1	3.329
	2	2.951		1	3.411
	1	2.957		1	3.487
	2	3.295		4	3.533
	2	3.329		1	3.664

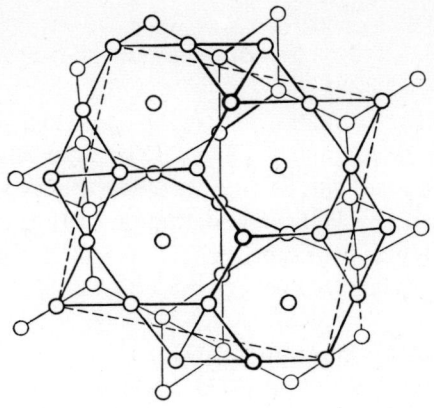

Fig. 2. Projection of the βU structure onto the (001) plane; the cell is marked by dash lines.

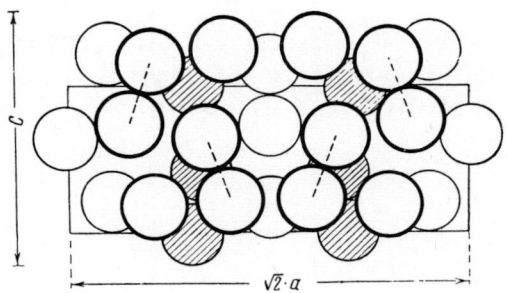

Fig. 3. Section of the βU cell along the (110) plane, after Thewlis and Steeple.

According to Thewlis and Steeple [10], the valence states of uranium atoms of different structural types in the βU crystal are as follows:

U_I	U_{II}	U_{III}	U_{IV}	U_V	U_{VI}
3	3	5	4	6	6

The valence of uranium is 4 in αU, and 3 in γU. Many of the interatomic distances given in Table 1 correspond to intermediate states of these valences.

The modern state of knowledge of the structure of βU is presented in a joint paper by Tucker, Senio, Thewlis, and Steeple [10a].

3. ɣU is stable from 774° to the melting point of uranium, 1132 ± 1° [3], McLennan and McKay [12] found in 1930 that ɣU has a cubic body-centered structure of the α Fe type; this was subsequently confirmed by Wilson and Rundle [13]. The most accurate value for the lattice constant of ɣU at 805° is probably given by Thewlis [14], according to whom a = 3.525 A.

Hence each uranium atom in ɣU has eight nearest neighbors at a distance of 3.05 A. Therefore the atomic radius of uranium in ɣU at 805° is 1.525 A.

NEPTUNIUM

1. αNp is stable at temperatures up to 278 ± 5°, according to Zachariasen [15]. The structure is rhombic, of unique type. The lattice constants are given in Table 2 [15].

TABLE 2

DIMENSIONS OF THE αNp UNIT CELL

Temperature, °C	Lattice constants, A		
	a	b	c
20	4.723 ± 0.001	4.887 ± 0.002	6.663 ± 0.003
212	4.746 ± 0.002	4.909 ± 0.003	6.704 ± 0.004
275	4.752 ± 0.002	4.920 ± 0.003	6.722 ± 0.004

The experimental density at 20° is 19.5 0.5 g/cc. The unit cell contains 8 atoms. Space group D_{2h}^{16} — Pmcn. Atomic coordinates: 4Np$_I$ in 4(c)$_I$: y_I = 0.208, z_I = 0.036; 4Np$_{II}$ in 4(c)$_{II}$: y_{II} = 0.842, z_{II} = 0.319.

The projection of the structure onto the (001) plane is given in Fig. 4. The interatomic distances and the numbers of nearest neighbors are:

Np_I — $1Np_{II}$ = 2.60 A Np_{II} — $1Np_I$ = 2.60 A
  — $1Np_{II}$ = 2.63   — $1Np_I$ = 2.63
  — $2Np_{II}$ = 2.64   — $2Np_I$ = 2.64
  — $1Np_{II}$ = 3.06   — $1Np_I$ = 3.06
  — $2Np_I$ = 3.16   — $2Np_I$ = 3.35
  — $2Np_I$ = 3.33   — $2Np_{II}$ = 3.44
  — $2Np_{II}$ = 3.35   — $4Np_{II}$ = 3.53

Each atom of Np_I and Np_{II} has four near neighbors of another kind at somewhat differing distances: 2.60, 2.63, and 2.64 A, probably corresponding to the partially covalent nature of interatomic bonding

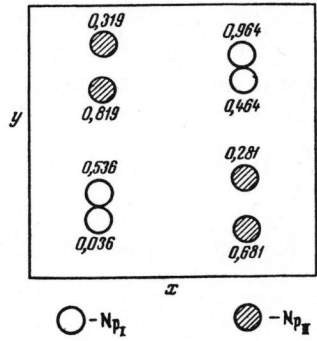

Fig. 4. Projection of the α Np structure onto the (001) plane; the numbers give the Z coordinates (height out of the paper).

αNp crystals. These four nearest bonds can be said to be directed approximately toward four out of the five corners of a trigonal bipyramid. However, these four angles are not the same for the atomic bonds in Np_I and Np_{II}; this is shown by continuous lines in Fig. 5 (after Zachariasen [15]).

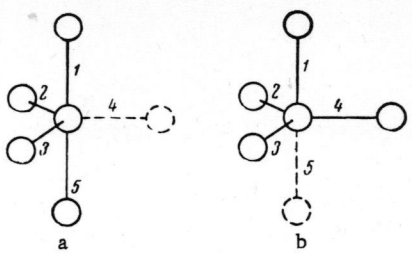

Fig. 5. Coordination around atoms of Np_I (a) and Np_{II} (b) in the structure of αNp.

The angles between the bonds denoted by the corresponding numbers in Fig. 5, and the corresponding data for U, are given below:

Bonds	Np_I	Np_{II}	αU
1—2	84°30'	90°30'	90°
1—3	84°30'	90°30'	90°
1—4	—	79°	—
2—3	127°	127°	127°
3—4	—	116°	—
4—2	—	116°	—
2—5	89°30'	—	90°
3—5	89°30'	—	90°

It is seen that the atomic configuration and bond angles of Np_I and αNp are similar to those in the αU structure. The atomic radius of neptunium in αNp, according to Zachariasen [15], is 1.50 A for coordination number 12.

2. βNp is stable, according to Zachariasen [15] between 278 and approximately 550°. The structure is tetragonal, layered, of the InBi type [16].

The lattice constants of βNp at different temperatures, from Zachariasen's data [15], are given in Table 3.

TABLE 3

DIMENSIONS OF THE βNp UNIT CELL

Temperature, °C	Lattice constants, Å	
	a	c
282	4.883±0.002	3.389±0.002
300	4.889	3.388
313	4.897	3.388
360	4.910	3.390
425	4.928	3.390
480	4.954	3.387
500	4.966	3.387

Space group D_4^2–$P42_1$. The unit cell contains four atoms with the coordinates: $2Np_I$ in: 000, $\frac{1}{2}\frac{1}{2}0$; $2Np_{II}$ in: $\frac{1}{2}0u$, $0\frac{1}{2}\bar{u}$; $u = 0.375 \pm \pm 0.015$.

The structure of βNp is a tetragonally distorted close-packed cubic type. If the axes a and c were equal and if u was 0.5, the structure would be cubic face-centered.

The numbers of nearest neighbors and their distances from Np_I and Np_{II} atoms in Np are given below (for 313°):

Np_I — $4Np_{II}$ = 2.76 Å Np_{II} — $4Np_I$ = 2.76 Å
   — $4Np_{II}$ = 3.24   — $4Np_I$ = 3.24
   — $2Np_I$ = 3.39   — $2Np_{II}$ = 3.39
   — $4Np_I$ = 3.46   — $4Np_{II}$ = 3.56

As in αNp, each atom in βNp has four nearest neighbors at a distance of 2.76 Å, covalently bonded. The coordination differs for Np_I and Np_{II} atoms. The four nearest Np_{II} atoms lie around the Np_I atom at the corners of a deformed tetrahedron with angles of 102° and 125° (at 313°). The four nearest Np_I atoms are attached to the Np_{II} atom on one side, and lie at the corners of a square with 3.46 A sides; the vertical distance from Np_{II} to the base of the square is 1.27 A, which corresponds to an angle of 78° between the bonds. The tetrahedrons of Np_{II} atoms, filled with Np_I atoms, are linked by their edges, forming infinite layers lying on top of each other perpendicular to the z axis.

3. γNp probably exists at temperatures above 550—570° up to the melting point at 640°, according to Zachariasen [15]. It has a cubic body-centered structure of the αFe type with the constant $a = 3.52$ A at 600°. The value of the lattice constant extrapolated to 20° is $a = 3.43$ A, which corresponds to the interatomic distance Np — 8Np = 2.97 A and an atomic radius of 1.48 A (at 20°) for γNp.

PLUTONIUM

1. αPu is stable at temperatures up to 122° [17]. The crystal structure of αPu was established by Zachariasen and Ellinger [105, 106]. The crystal system is monoclinic. The dimensions of the unit cell of αPu at 21° are: $a = 6.1835 \pm 0.0005$ A; $b = 4.8244 \pm 0.0005$ A; $c = 10.973 \pm 0.001$ A; $\beta = 101.81° \pm 0.02°$. The unit cell contains 16 atoms. Space group C_{2h}^2 — $P2_1/m$. All the atoms are situated in eight two-fold positions $\pm (x, \frac{1}{4}, z)$. The structural varieties Pu_I—Pu_{VIII} have the following approximate atomic parameters: for Pu_I $x = 0.332$, $z = 0.152$; for Pu_{II} $x = 0.767$, $z = 0.169$; for Pu_{III} $x = 138$, $z = 0.337$; for Pu_{IV} $x = 0.651$, $z = 456$; for Pu_V $x = 0.013$, $z = 0.617$; for Pu_{VI} $x = 0.459$, $z = 0.642$; for Pu_{VII} $x = 0.335$, $z = 0.924$; and for Pu_{VIII} $x = 0.885$, $z = 0.897$. The calculated density is 19.816 ± 0.006 g/cc. The experimental density of αPu at 25° is 19.737 g/cc. The coordination number is 14 for most plutonium atoms, with average interatomic distance 3.20 A. The coordination number of Pu_I is 12, with average interatomic distance 3.11 A. The coordination number of Pu_{VIII} is 16, with average interatomic distance 3.31 A. Each Pu atom has four short bonds, of average length 2.64 A, with the exceptions of Pu_{VII} and Pu_I atoms, which have three and five nearest neighbors each respectively.

2. βPu is stable from 122 to 203° [17]. The crystal structure has not been determined. The density at 150° is 17.65 g/cc.

3. γPu is stable in the temperature range from 203 to 317° [17]. According to Zachariasen and Ellinger [18], the structure is rhombic, of unique type.

The lattice constants at various temperatures are given in Table 4 [18]. The x-ray density of γPu at 210° is 17.19 g/cc.

TABLE 4

DIMENSIONS OF THE γPu UNIT CELL

Temperature, °C	Lattice constants, A		
	a	b	c
213 ± 2	3.16052	5.76275	10.1442
233	3.15909	5.76769	10.1615
258	3.15622	5.77371	10.1834
312	3.15397	5.78574	10.2290

An interesting fact is that the coefficient of thermal expansion of γPu in the [100] direction is negative, as is shown by the data in Table 4.

Space group D_{2h}^{24} —Fddd. The unit cell contains eight structurally equivalent atoms, occupying a regular system of 8 (a) points, with the coordinates: 000, $0\frac{1}{2}\frac{1}{2}$, $\frac{1}{2}0\frac{1}{2}$, $\frac{1}{2}\frac{1}{2}0$, $\frac{111}{444}$, $\frac{331}{444}$, $\frac{313}{444}$, $\frac{133}{444}$. The projection of the structure of γPu onto the (001) face is shown in Fig. 6.

If all the three edges of the γPu unit cell were equal, it would have a structure of the diamond type. However, in reality the lattice constants differ very greatly, and this leads to a new atomic coordination in γPu, not found in any other element. Each plutonium atom is surrounded by ten neighboring atoms at approximately equal distances: Pu -- 4Pu = 3.026 A; Pu -- 2Pu = 3.159 A; Pu -- 4Pu = 3.288 A.

Nevertheless, at the nearest distance of 3.026 A there are only four neighboring atoms, situated at the vertices of a distorted tetrahedron; this is reminiscent of the coordination patterns in α and β neptunium. However, in γ Pu the tetrahedrons form a continuous diamondlike spatial structure. Pseudohexagonal atomic layers with interatomic distances of 3.159 and 3.288 A within the layers, and with 3.026 A the closest distance between the layers, lie normally to the c axis. These pseudohexagonal layers are reminiscent, on the other hand, of the corresponding coordination patterns in α and β uranium.

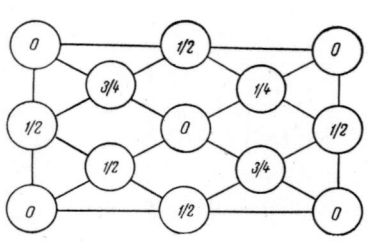

Fig. 6. Projection of the γ Pu structure onto the (001) face, after Zachariasen and Ellinger; the numbers indicate the Z coordinates.

The atomic radius of γPu, with a coordination correction, is 1.60 A according to Zachariasen [18].

4. δPu is stable between 317 and 453°, according to Jette [17]. The crystal structure is cubic, face-centered, of the Cu type. The lattice constant at 320° is $a = 4.6370$ A. Each atom has 12 nearest neighbors at a distance of 3.279 A. The atomic radius of δPu is 1.64 A. The x-ray density of δPu at 320° is 15.92 g/cc. A very interesting fact is that δPu, with the lowest density of all plutonium modifications, has the most closely packed crystal structure. Still more striking is the fact that the coefficient of thermal expansion of δPu is negative, i.e., when heated in the 317--453° range δPu does not expand like all normal metals, but contracts. The coefficient of linear expansion $\alpha = -10.0 \times 10^{-6}$ degree^{-1}. This anomaly is even more pronounced in the next high-temperature modification of plutonium, δ'Pu.

5. δ'Pu is stable in a narrow temperature range, from 453 to 477° [17]. The crystal structure is tetragonal, face-centered, of the γMn type, with four atoms in the cell. At 465° the cell constants are: $a=$ 4.701 A; $c=$ 4.489 A; $c/a=$ 0.955. The x-ray density is 15.99 g/cc. The coefficient of linear expansion $\alpha = -120 \times 10^{-6}$ degree^{-1}.

6. εPu is stable from 477° to the melting point, which is 639.5 ± 2° C [17]. The structure is cubic, body-centered, of the αFe type. The lattice constant $a=$ 3.638 A at 500°. The x-ray density is 16.48 g/cc. Each atom has eight nearest neighbors at a distance of 3.150 A. The atomic radius of εPu is 1.58 A. A very interesting fact is that the density of εPu is considerably greater than the densities of δPu and δ'Pu, which are stable at lower temperatures and are more closely packed.

OTHER ACTINIDE ELEMENTS

Of the other actinide elements, protactinium and americium have known crystal structures.

Protactinium has tetragonal body-centered structure with two atoms in the unit cell, which has the dimensions: $a=$ 3.925 A, $c=$ 3.238 A [112]. The atomic radius of protactinium in the metallic state is 1.63 A.

Americium has hexagonal structure with lattice constants: $a=$ 3.642 A, $c=$ 11.76 A [113]. The cell contains four americium atoms of two structural kinds. Space group D_{6h}^4 —C6/mmc, atomic coordinates: 2 Am$_I$ in 000, 00$\frac{1}{2}$; 2 Am$_{II}$ in $\frac{123}{334}$, $\frac{211}{334}$.

The atomic radius of metallic americium is 1.82 A. The polymorphism of americium has not been studied.

The crystal structure of the transamericium elements is as yet unknown.

IV. CRYSTAL STRUCTURE OF SIMPLE COMPOUNDS OF URANIUM, THORIUM, PLUTONIUM, AND NEPTUNIUM

In our consideration of the crystal structures of simple compounds of uranium, thorium, plutonium, and neptunium with other chemical elements, the emphasis is on descriptions of new structural types and on elucidation of their atomic coordination and interatomic distances.

By simple compounds we mean compounds or phases belonging to binary equilibrium systems of two components, represented by the corresponding phase diagrams. One of the components is thorium, uranium, plutonium, or neptunium, and the other can be any of the other chemical elements in Mendeleev's periodic system. Our considerations are based on the expanded form of Mendeleev's periodic system which, as is clear from Fig. 7, divides the chemical elements into metals, semimetals, and nonmetals most distinctly.

On the basis of the table in Fig. 7, all chemical elements may be divided into the following groups:

1) The alkali and alkaline-earth metals, contained in subgroups Ia and IIa;

2) transition elements: lanthanides and actinides, contained in subgroup IIIa;

3) transition elements: ordinary metals, contained in subgroups IVa, Va, VIa, VIIa, VIII and Ib;

Ia	IIa	IIIa															IVa	Va	VIa	VIIa	VIII			Ib	IIb	IIIb	IVb	Vb	VIb	VIIb	0
																														1 H 0,46	2 He
3 Li 1,55																									4 Be 1,12	5 B 0,98	6 C 0,91	7 N 0,88	8 O	9 F	10 Ne
11 Na 1,89																									12 Mg 1,60	13 Al 1,43	14 Si 1,32	15 P 1,28	16 S 1,27	17 Cl	18 A
19 K 2,35	20 Ca 1,97	21 Sc 1,62															22 Ti 1,47	23 V 1,34	24 Cr 1,27	25 Mn 1,26	26 Fe 1,26	27 Co 1,25	28 Ni 1,24	29 Cu 1,28	30 Zn 1,38	31 Ga 1,41	32 Ge 1,37	33 As 1,39	34 Se 1,40	35 Br	36 Kr
37 Rb 2,48	38 Sr 2,15	39 Y 1,80															40 Zr 1,60	41 Nb 1,46	42 Mo 1,39	43 Tc 1,37	44 Ru 1,34	45 Rh 1,34	46 Pd 1,37	47 Ag 1,44	48 Cd 1,54	49 In 1,66	50 Sn 1,54	51 Sb 1,59	52 Te 1,60	53 I	54 Xe
55 Cs 2,67	56 Ba 2,21	57 La 1,87	58 Ce 1,82	59 Pr 1,82	60 Nd 1,82	61 Pm	62 Sm 1,85	63 Eu 2,08	64 Gd 1,80	65 Tb 1,77	66 Dy 1,77	67 Ho 1,76	68 Er 1,75	69 Tm 1,74	70 Yb 1,93	71 Lu 1,74	72 Hf 1,59	73 Ta 1,46	74 W 1,39	75 Re 1,37	76 Os 1,35	77 Ir 1,36	78 Pt 1,39	79 Au 1,44	80 Hg 1,57	81 Tl 1,71	82 Pb 1,75	83 Bi 1,70	84 Po 1,76	85 At	86 Rn
87 Fr	88 Ra	89 Ac	90 T 1,80	91 Pa 1,63	92 U 1,52	93 Np 1,50	94 Pu 1,60	95 Am 1,82	96 Cm	97 Bk	**98 Cf**	**99 E**	**100 Fm**	101 Md																	

Fig. 7. Expanded form of Mendeleev's periodic system of the elements.

4) elements of the b subgroups, contained in subgroups IIb, IIIb, IVb, Vb, VIb, and VIIb, including semimetals and nonmetals.

The atomic radii are given in kX, after Pauling [6], correct to the second decimal place for the low-temperature modification under the symbol for each element.

The following explanations are necessary for Tables (5—15, 17—23) of experimental data, given below.

These tables summarize data on the compounds formed, with their chemical formulas and types of crystal structure, arranged by the subgroups of the periodic table shown in Fig. 7.

The summaries are based on literature data; the relevant literature references are indicated in a separate column in each table.

If compounds are not formed, appropriate signs are used to indicate the nature of component interaction in the given system. The sign ⌒ indicates phase separation into layers in the liquid state. A dash (—) indicates absence of compound formation and of appreciable regions of solid solutions. The symbols "eut" and "perit" indicate simple eutectic or peritectic character of the phase diagram without formation of compounds or considerable regions of α solid solutions. If considerable regions of solid solutions based on one of the components are formed, the maximum concentration of the dissolved component (in atomic percentages) is noted; for example, γU—40 Mo means that γU dissolves 40 atomic % of Mo at a temperature which the reader must determine from the original literature source, noted by a number to the right of each square. If any components of a given system form a continuous series of solid solutions, the corresponding symbols for the modifications of the elements are joined by a dash; e.g., γU—βZr. If new phases, usually of variable composition, are formed from solid solutions on decrease of temperature, then they are denoted by the Greek letters used in the original source, the homogeneity limits being indicated if possible. An empty square means that the system has not been studied, or studied very inadequately. New structural types found for actinide compounds are enclosed in frames.

SUBGROUPS Ia, IIa, IIIa

It is clear from Tables 5, 6, 7, and 8 that the systems of alloys of the alkali and alkaline-earth metals, lanthanides, and actinides with thorium, uranium, plutonium, and neptunium have been studied very inadequately. However, the available tabulated data appear to be characteristic for all the considered systems of these subgroups. They indicate that chemical interaction between the components in such systems is very limited. This results in almost total immiscibility in the liquid and solid states, and to absence of chemical compounds.

An exception seems to be alloys of actinides with each other; here, because of the similarity of their 5f electron structure the formation of wide regions of liquid and solid solutions, and of chemical compounds, is to be expected. Confirmation for this is provided by the only system studied so far: uranium--plutonium, where, according to available data [21], the compounds Pu_3U and PuU with large unit cells have been found. Pu_3U is tetragonal: $a=$ 10.57 A; $c=$ 10.76 A; the cell contains 52 atoms. PuU is cubic, primitive, $a=$ 10.664 A; the cell contains 58 atoms. The atomic arrangement has not been established.

It is noteworthy that thorium does not mix with uranium either in the liquid or the solid state, the system showing phase separation; this is indicative of differences in the electron structures of the two metals. This fact appears to provide indirect evidence for the absence of 5f electrons in thorium in the metallic state, the electron structure of which can be regarded, according to Seaborg [57], as $6d^2 7s^2$. Thus, thorium occupies a somewhat distinct position in the actinide group, and by its chemical properties it is the analog of the "d-elements" of the IVa subgroup: Hf, Zr, and Ti, rather than a member of the "5f" elements. It is shown later that this conclusion is confirmed by further considerations of the crystal-chemical behavior of thorium with metals of other subgroups.

SUBGROUPS IVa, Va, VIa

The elements of the IVa, Va, and VIa subgroups show some common crystal-chemical features in their interaction with thorium,

TABLE 5

SUBGROUP Ia

	Li	Lit. source	Na	Lit. source	K	Lit. source	Rb	Lit. source	Cs	Lit. source	Fr	Lit. source
Th			◊	[19]								
U			—	[20]								
Pu												
Np												

TABLE 6

SUBGROUP IIa

	Ca	Lit. source	Sr	Lit. source	Ba	Lit. source	Ra	Lit. source
Th								
U	—	[20]						
Pu								
Np								

TABLE 7

SUBGROUP IIIa AND LANTHANIDES

	Sc	Y	La	Ce	Pr	Nd	Pm	Sm	Eu	Gd	Tb	Dy	Ho	Er	Tm	Yb	Lu
Th			[19]	[19]													
U			[20]	[20]	[20]	[20]											
Pu																	
Np																	

TABLE 8

SUBGROUP IIIa AND ACTINIDES

	Ac	Th	Pa	U	Np	Pu	Am	Cm	Bk	Cf	E	Fm	Md
Th		αTh βTh		[20]									
U				αU βU γU									
Pu				Pu$_3$U PuU [21]		αPu δPu βPu δ'Pu γPu εPu							
Np					αNp βNp γNp								

uranium, and plutonium (systems with neptunium have not been studied), and we therefore consider them as a single group. It is clear from Tables 9, 10, and 11 that the most general characteristic feature of this group is complete miscibility of the components of this group in the liquid melted state; this distinguishes

TABLE 9

SUBGROUP IVa

	Ti			Zr			Hf		
	Formula of compound	Structure type	Lit. source	Formula of compound	Structure type	Lit. source	Formula of compound	Structure type	Lit. source
Th	эвт.		[19]	βTh—βZr	αFe	[19]	βTh—βHf	αFe	[19]
U	γU—βTi U₂Ti	αFe AlB₂, BiIn₂?	[20] [22] [116]	γU—βZr δ(U—Zr) (54—85% Zr)	αFe AlB₂? BiIn₂?	[20] [23] [114] [24] [115] [116]			
Pu				Pu$_x$Zr (x>3)		[21]			
Np									

the group from the previous group, containing elements of the Ia, IIa, and IIIa subgroups, where phase separation was the general rule. This is a sign of more active chemical interaction between the components in these systems, probably because of the greater similarity of the external electron structures of their atoms. This conclusion is confirmed by the behavior of melts during crystallization, since the solid-state reactions observed here are characteristic of the phase diagrams of elements contained in the same subgroup of the periodic system, and characterized by analogous structures of the external electron shells of their atoms.

TABLE 10

SUBGROUP Va

	V			Nb			Ta		
	Formula of compound	Structure type	Lit. source	Formula of compound	Structure type	Lit. source	Formula of compound	Structure type	Lit. source
Th	eut.		[19]	eut.		[19]			
U	eut.		[20]	$\gamma U - Nb$	αFe	[20]	perit.		[20]
Pu	eut.		[47]						
Np									

TABLE 11

SUBGROUP VIa

	Cr			Mo			W		
	Formula of compound	Structure type	Lit. source	Formula of compound	Structure type	Lit. source	Formula of compound	Structure type	Lit. source
Th	eut.		[19]				eut.		[19]
U	eut.		[20]	$\gamma U - 40Mo$ $\delta (U - Mo)$ (28–31%Mo)	αFe $AlCr_2$	[20] [109] [23, 25]	perit.		[20]
Pu	eut.		[47]						
Np									

Indeed, crystallization of melts in the systems in question is accompanied by either eutectic or peritectic interaction with formation of limited α solutions and mechanical mixtures of these, or by formation of continuous series of solid solutions of the high-temperature modifications of the components; when the temperature is lowered the solid solutions more often undergo eutectoid or peritectoid decomposition, and sometimes give rise to regions of ordered phases, which arise only after prolonged low-temperature annealing.

Eutectic and peritectic phase diagrams are characteristic of the following systems: thorium–titanium, thorium–vanadium, thorium–niobium, thorium–chromium, thorium–tungsten [19], uranium–vanadium, uranium–tantalum, uranium–chromium, uranium–molybdenum, uranium–tungsten [20], plutonium–vanadium, plutonium–chromium [47]. More or less limited solid solutions, usually of the high-temperature modifications of the elements, are formed in these systems.

The greatest tendency to form solid solutions is shown by γU. Thus, in the system uranium–molybdenum, γU can dissolve up to 40 atomic % of Mo [20, 23]; in the concentration region of 28–31 atomic % Mo, prolonged low-temperature annealing (at 400–500°) results in the formation of an ordered γ′ (or δ) phase, stable at room temperature [25]. The γ′ phase (U–Mo) has the ideal composition MoU_2, and has a tetragonal body-centered structure of the $AlCr_2$ type [109], which is a peculiar superstructure derived from the CsCl type with an approximately trebled lattice constant along the c axis. The lattice constants are: a = 3.427 Å; c = 9.834 Å; c/a = 2.871 [109].

Continuous regions of solid solutions have been found for the systems: βTh – βZr, βTh – βHf [19], γU – βTi, γU – βZr, γU – βNb [20]. In the system uranium–zirconium below 600° the high-temperature region of γU – βZr solid solutions yields an ordered δ phase, lying in the range of 53 to 85 atomic % Zr [23]. According to Mueller [24, 114] the δ (U – Zr) phase has a cubic structure with 54 atoms in the cell, with constant a = 10.688 Å; this is treble the edge of the cubic cell of the γU – βZr parent solid solution. The atomic arrangement in the structure of δ (U – Zr) has not been established, but there are indications that UZr$_2$ has a hexagonal disordered structure of the AlB$_2$ type [115] or, possibly, a structure of the BiIn$_2$ type [116], characterized by doubling of the lattice constant along the z axis as compared with the AlB$_2$ type and an ordered atomic arrangement.

In the region of YU — βTi solid solutions a prolonged annealing at temperatures below 850° leads to formation of an ordered phase of variable composition based on the compound TiU$_2$, lying within the approximate range of 32 to 42 atomic % Ti at 500°, and stable at room temperature [58]. According to Knapton [22], TiU$_2$ has a hexagonal structure of the AlB$_2$ type with the constants a = 4.828 A, c = 2.847 A, c/a = 0.589, or possibly a structure of the BiIn$_2$ type [116].

Analysis of the results given in Tables 9, 10, and 11 leads to the conclusion that in the systems under consideration the greatest tendency to chemical interaction with the actinides is shown by elements of subgroup IVa: titanium, zirconium, and hafnium.

Although there do not seem to have been any special experimental investigations in order to determine the structural type of the solid solutions, it may be said with confidence that all the indicated cases for these subgroups belong to substitutional solid solutions, since the components are isomorphous at high temperatures. Evidence for this is provided by the regular variation of the lattice constants with changes in the composition of the solid solutions.

Thus, the characteristic crystal-chemical feature of this group of systems is that the atoms retain their original coordination and the numbers of nearest neighbors within the limits of limited or unlimited solid solutions at high temperatures, with formation of ordered phases—superlattices (rarely)—or mechanical mixtures of the components (more often) at low temperatures. The character of the structures is predominantly homodesmic [59], i.e., homogeneous with regard to the type of interatomic bonding.

SUBGROUPS VIIa, VIII

The formation of typical intermetallides with characteristic close-packed structure commences with the manganese subgroup (VIIa).

It is clear from Tables 12–15 that the number of compounds formed gradually increases from the manganese subgroup to the nickel subgroup. This relationship, which was first observed for plutonium alloys by S. T. Konobeevskii [47] apparently holds for all the systems considered in these subgroups.

The systems which have been studied most fully in the crystal-chemical sense are systems formed by the actinide metals (except neptunium) with the first members of these subgroups: manganese, iron, cobalt, and nickel. Systems with the noble metals have hardly been studied at all, while systems with the artificial element, technetium, are unlikely ever to be studied.

Of *known** structural types, the following are represented in the group of systems under consideration:

$MgCu_2$ type: UMn_2 ($a = 7.1628$ A); $PuMn_2$ ($a = 7.29$ A); UFe_2 ($a = 7.058$ A); $PuFe_2$ ($a = 7.179$ A); UCo_2 ($a = 6.9924$ A); $PuCo_2$ ($a = 7.075$ A); $PuNi_2$ ($a = 7.14$ A); UOs_2 ($a = 7.498$ A); UIr_2 ($a = 7.494$ A).

$MgZn_2$ type: $ThMn_2$ ($a = 5.48$; $c = 8.95$ A); UNi_2 ($a = 4.966$; $c = 8.252$ A); $PuOs_2$ ($a = 5.326$; $c = 8.665$ kX).

$PdBe_5$ type: UNi_5 ($a = 6.783$ A; $x = \frac{5}{8}$).

$CaZn_5$ type: $ThFe_5$ ($a = 5.13$; $c = 4.02$ A); $ThCo_5$ ($a = 5.01$; $c = 3.97$ A); $ThNi_4$ ($a = 4.97$; $c = 4.01$ A); $PuNi_5$ ($a = 4.87$; $c = 3.97$ A).

$AuCu_3$ type. URu_3 ($a = 3.980$ kX).

---

* Here and subsequently we include in known structural types all those structural types on which data have been published in handbooks [82] up to 1941.

TABLE 12

SUBGROUP VIIa

	Mn			Tc			Re		
	Formula of compound	Structure type	Lit. source	Formula of compound	Structure type	Lit. source	Formula of compound	Structure type	Lit. source
Th	ThMn$_2$ Th$_6$Mn$_{23}$ ThMn$_{12}$	MgZn$_2$ Th$_6$Mn$_{23}$ ThMn$_{12}$	[26] [26] [26] [19]						
U	U$_6$Mn UMn$_2$	U$_6$Mn MgCu$_2$	[27] [27]						
Pu	PuMn$_2$	MgCu$_2$	[21, 47, 60]						
Np									

TABLE 13

SUBGROUP VIII$_{Fe}$

	Fe			Ru			Os		
	Formula of compound	Structure type	Lit. source	Formula of compound	Structure type	Lit. source	Formula of compound	Structure type	Lit. source
Th	Th$_7$Fe$_3$	Th$_7$Ni$_3$	[28]						
	ThFe$_3$	?	[28]						
	ThFe$_5$	CaZn$_5$	[28]						
	Th$_2$Fe$_{17}$	Th$_2$Fe$_{17}$	[28]						
U	U$_6$Fe	U$_6$Mn	[28]	URu$_3$	AuCu$_3$	[29]	UOs$_2$	MgCu$_2$	[29]
	UFe$_2$	MgCu$_2$	[27]						
Pu	Pu$_6$Fe	U$_6$Mn	[21]				η (Pu — Os)	?	[47]
	PuFe$_2$	MgCu$_2$	[21, 47, 60]				θ (Pu — Os)	?	[47]
							Pu$_5$Os$_3$	?	[47]
							PuOs$_3$	MgZn$_2$	[47]
Np									

TABLE 14

SUBGROUP VIII$_{Co}$

		Co			Rh			Ir		
	Formula of compound	Structure type	Lit. source	Formula of compound	Structure type	Lit. source	Formula of compound	Structure type	Lit. source
Th	Th$_7$Co$_3$ ThCo ThCo$_{2\rightarrow 3}$ ThCo$_5$ Th$_2$Co$_{17}$	Th$_7$Ni$_3$ ThCo ? CaZn$_5$ Th$_2$Fe$_{17}$	[28] [28] [28] [28] [28]						
U	U$_6$Co UCo$_2$ UCo	U$_6$Mn MgCu$_2$ UCo	[27] [27] [27]				UIr$_2$	MgCu$_2$	[29]
Pu	Pu$_6$Co Pu$_2$Co PuCo$_2$ PuCo$_3$ Pu$_2$Co$_{17}$	U$_6$Mn Fe$_2$P? MgCu$_2$? Th$_2$Ni$_{17}$	[108] [108] [24, 60] [108] [108]						
Np									

TABLE 15

SUBGROUP VIII$_{Ni}$

	Formula of compound	Ni			Pd			Pt		
		Formula of compound	Structure type	Lit. source	Formula of compound	Structure type	Lit. source	Formula of compound	Structure type	Lit. source
Th		Th$_7$Ni$_3$ ThNi ThNi$_2$ ThNi$_4$→$_5$ Th$_2$Ni$_{17}$	Th$_7$Ni$_3$ ThNi AlB$_2$ CaZn$_5$ Th$_2$Ni$_{17}$	[28] [28] [30] [28] [28]						
U		U$_6$Ni UNi U$_7$Ni$_9$ U$_5$Ni$_7$ UNi$_2$ UNi$_5$	U$_6$Mn ? ? ? MgZn$_2$ PdBe$_5$	[27] [27] [31] [31] [27] [27]	UPd$_3$	Ni$_3$Ti	[29]	UPt$_3$	Ni$_3$Sn	[29]
Pu		PuNi PuNi$_2$ PuNi$_3$ PuNi$_4$ PuNi$_5$ Pu$_2$Ni$_{17}$	? MgCu$_2$? ? CaZn$_5$ Th$_2$Ni$_{17}$	[47] [21; 47; 60] [21] [21] [21, 47, 60] [21, 60]						
Np										

Ni$_3$Sn type: UPt$_3$ (a = 5.752; c = 4.889 kX).

Ni$_3$Ti type: UPd$_3$ (a = 5.757; c = 9.621 kX).

AlB$_2$ type: ThNi$_2$ (a = 3.96; c = 3.83 A).

All these structures fit into the first groups of the crystal-chemical classification of metallic phases (see p. 16), and are also characterized [61] by "superclose" atomic packing conforming to the principle: "the total coordination number of nearest neighbors exceeds 12."

Next we consider atomic coordination in new* structural types, found among compounds of manganese, iron, cobalt, and nickel with thorium, uranium, and plutonium, namely: Th$_7$Ni$_3$; ThCo; ThNi; Th$_2$Ni$_{17}$; Th$_2$Fe$_{17}$; U$_6$Mn; UCo; Th$_6$Mn$_{23}$; ThMn$_{12}$.

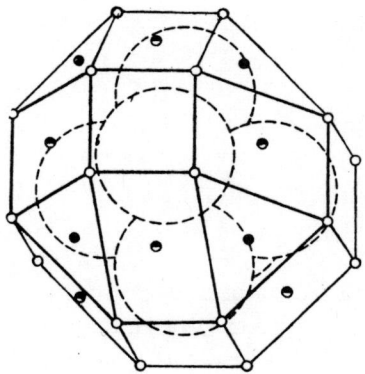

Fig. 8. Atomic coordination in Th$_6$Mn$_{23}$, after Florio, Rundle, and Snow.
Large dash circles — Th atoms; small white circles — Mn$_{II}$ atoms; black and white circles — Mn$_{IV}$ atoms; black circles — Mn$_{III}$ atoms.

---

* Here and subsequently we include in new structural types all those on which data have been published since the war.

1. Th_6Mn_{23} type [26]. The structure is cubic. Th_6Mn_{23} is the sole representative. Lattice constant $a = 12.523 \pm 0.001$ A. The unit cell contains four groups as represented by the formula. Space group O_h^5 — Fm3m; atomic coordinates 24 (e) Th, $x = 0.203$; 4 (b) Mn_I; 24 (d) Mn_{II}; 32 (f) Mn_{III}, $x = 0.378$; 32 (f) Mn_{IV}, $x = 0.178$. By the nature of the atomic arrangement, $ThMn_{23}$ belongs to the coordination class*.

The thorium atoms form octahedrons which are grouped around the four face-centering positions of the unit cell. Each such octahedron, surrounded by 44 manganese atoms, forms the complex polyhedron shown in Fig. 8.

The coordination numbers and interatomic distances (in A) are:

$$
\begin{array}{llll}
Th & - 4Th & = 3.59 & \quad Mn_{III} - 3Th = 3.08 \\
   & - 4Mn_{III} & = 3.08 & \quad\quad\quad - 3Mn_{IV} = 2.69 \\
   & - 4Mn_{IV} & = 3.16 & \quad\quad\quad - 3Mn_{II} = 2.73 \\
   & - 4Mn_{II} & = 3.18 & \quad\quad\quad - 3Mn_{III} = 3.05 \\
Mn_I & - 6Th & = 3.71 & \quad\quad\quad - 1Mn_I = 2.64 \\
   & - 8Mn_{III} & = 2.64 & \quad Mn_{IV} - 3Th = 3.16 \\
MnII & - 4Th & = 3.18 & \quad\quad\quad - 3Mn_{IV} = 2.55 \\
   & - 4Mn_{IV} & = 2.56 & \quad\quad\quad - 3Mn_{II} = 2.56 \\
   & - 4Mn_{III} & = 2.73 & \quad\quad\quad - 3Mn_{III} = 2.69 \\
\end{array}
$$

Each thorium atom has a total coordination number of 16 = 4Th + + 12 Mn. Manganese has four different structural varieties, each with its characteristic and generally complex coordination, also with high coordination numbers.

Thus, the considerable difference between the atomic radii of thorium (1.80 A) and manganese (1.27 A), and the mainly metallic nature of the interatomic bonding ensure "superclose" atomic packing in the $ThMn_{23}$ structure, on the principle: coordination number $\geqslant 12$, without formation of any predominantly directed

---
* In accordance with the concepts of crystal chemistry [59], we shall distinguish (see also p. 7) the coordination, layer, chain, molecular (island) and mixed classes of crystal structure.

Th — Th or Th — Mn bonds. The Mn — Mn bonds are more complex, and apparently correspond to several valence states of manganese.

2. ThMn$_{12}$ type [26]. The structure is tetragonal, body-centered, with two formula units in the unit cell. The lattice constants of ThMn$_{12}$ are: $a =$ 8.74 ± 0.001 A; $c =$ 4.95 ± 0.01 A. Space group D_{4h}^{17} — J4/mmm; atomic coordinates: 2 (a) Th; 8 (f) Mn$_I$; 8 (i) Mn$_{II}$, $x =$ 0.361; 8 (j) Mn$_{III}$, $x =$ 0.277.

The ThMn$_{12}$ structure belongs to the coordination class. The thorium atoms, being in the 000 and $\frac{1}{2}\frac{1}{2}\frac{1}{2}$, positions, are not in contact with each other. Each thorium atom is surrounded by 20 manganese atoms, as shown in Fig. 9.

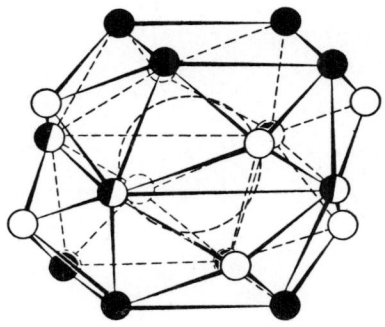

Fig. 9. Atomic coordination in ThMn$_{12}$, after Florio, Rundle, and Snow.
Large dash circle is Th; small circles: white, Mn$_I$; black and white, Mn$_{II}$; black, Mn$_{III}$.

The manganese atoms are of three structural kinds.

The coordination numbers and interatomic distances (A) are:

$$
\begin{aligned}
\text{Th} &- 4\text{Mn}_{II} = 3.15 & \text{Mn}_{II} &- 4\text{Mn}_{I} = 2.70\\
&- 8\text{Mn}_{III} = 3.15 & &- 2\text{Mn}_{III} = 2.76\\
&- 8\text{Mn}_{I} = 3.33 & &- 2\text{Mn}_{III} = 2.73\\
& & &- 4\text{Mn}_{II} = 3.02\\
\text{Mn}_{I} &- 4\text{Mn}_{III} = 2.53 & &- 1\text{Th} = 3.15\\
&- 4\text{Mn}_{II} = 2.70 & &- 1\text{Mn}_{II} = 2.42\\
&- 2\text{Th} = 3.33 & & \\
&- 2\text{Mn}_{I} = 2.48 & \text{Mn}_{III} &- 2\text{Th} = 3.15\\
& & &- 4\text{Mn}_{I} = 2.53\\
& & &- 2\text{Mn}_{II} = 2.76\\
& & &- 2\text{Mn}_{II} = 2.73\\
& & &- 2\text{Mn}_{III} = 2.73\\
\end{aligned}
$$

As in the previous instance, the $ThMn_{12}$ structure conforms to the principle: coordination number $\geqslant 12$.

3. Th_7Ni_3 type [28]. The structure is hexagonal, with two formula units in the unit cell. The lattice constants (in Å) for the three isomorphous compounds are:

	Th_7Fe_3	Th_7Co_3	Th_7Ni_3
a	9.85	9.83	9.86
c	6.15	6.17	6.23

Space group C_{6v}^4 — C6mc. Atomic coordinates: $2Th_I$ in 2(b), $z_I = 0.06$; $6Th_{II}$ in 6(c), $x_{II} = 0.126$; $z_{II} = 0.250$; $6Th_{III}$ in 6(c), $x_{III} = 0.544$, $z_{III} = 0.03$; 6Ni in 6(c), $x_{IV} = 0.815$, $z_{IV} = 0.31$.

The projection of the Th_7Ni_3 structure type onto the (0001) basal plane is shown in Fig. 10, with the z parameters rounded off.

The structure belongs to the coordination class. The coordination numbers and interatomic distances (in Å) for Th_7Fe_3 are given below:

Th_I — $2Fe$ = 2.89 Th_{III} — $3Fe$ = 2.96
— $2Fe$ = 2.90   — $3Th_{II}$ = 3.60
— $2Th_{II}$ = 3.55   — $3Th_{II}$ = 3.70
— $2Th_I$ = 3.72
— $4Th_I$ = 3.80 Fe — $2Th_I$ = 2.89
                    — $1Th_I$ = 2.90
Th_{II} — $2Fe$ = 2.91   — $2Th_{II}$ = 2.91
— $2Th_{II}$ = 3.43   — $1Th_{III}$ = 2.96
— $2Th_I$ = 3.55
— $1Th_{III}$ = 3.60
— $1Th_{III}$ = 3.70
— $2Th_{II}$ = 3.76

It has been pointed out [28] that the atomic parameters for the Th_7Ni_3 type require more precise determination, and at the present time it can be regarded only as approximate.

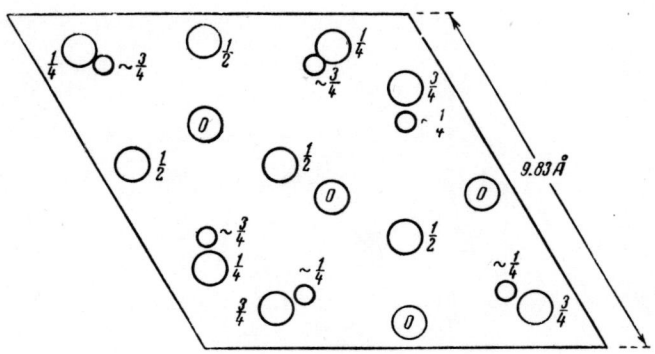

Fig. 10. Projection of the Th_7Ni_3 structure onto the (0001) plane, after Florio, Baenziger, and Rundle.
Large circles — Th atoms; small circles — Ni atoms.

4. ThCo type [28]. The structure is rhombic, with four formula units in the unit cell. The only representative, ThCo, has the following lattice constants: a = 3.74 A; b = 10.88 A; c = 4.16 A.

Space group: D_{2h}^{17} -- Cmcm; atomic coordinates: 4Th in 4(c), y_{Th} = 0.136; 4Co in 4(c), y_{Co} = 0.416.

The projection of the ThCo structure onto the (001) cell face is shown in Fig. 11; the large circles represent thorium and the small, cobalt atoms; black corresponds to z = 0.25, and white, to z = 0.75.

The coordination numbers and interatomic distances (A) are:

$$\begin{array}{ll} \text{Th} -- 6\text{Th} = 3.62 & \text{Co} -- 4\text{Th} = 2.86 \\ -- 2\text{Th} = 3.74 & -- 3\text{Th} = 3.04 \\ -- 4\text{Co} = 2.86 & -- 2\text{Co} = 2.77 \\ -- 3\text{Co} = 3.04 & \end{array}$$

Against a general background of a close-packed coordination structure for ThCo (total coordination number ⩾ 12) there are four strong Th -- Co bonds, considerably shorter (2.86 A) than the sum of the atomic radii of thorium and cobalt (3.05 A).

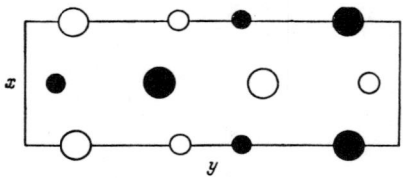

Fig. 11. Projection of the ThCo structure onto the (001) plane, after Florio, Baenziger, and Rundle.
Large and small black circles — Th and Co atoms with z = $1/4$; white circles — Th and Co atoms with z = $3/4$.

5. ThNi type [28]. The structure is rhombic, with eight formula units in the cell. The only representative is ThNi. Lattice constants: $a = 14.51$ A; $b = 4.31$ A; $c = 5.73$ A. Space group: D_{2h}^{16} -- Pnma; atomic coordinates: $4Th_I$ in 4(c); $x_1 = 0.094$, $z_1 = 0.140$; $4Th_{II}$ in 4(c): $x_2 = 0.344$, $z_2 = 0.140$; $4Ni_I$ in 4(c): $x_3 = 0.268$, $z_3 = 0.630$; $4Ni_{II}$ in 4(c): $x_4 = 0.518$, $z_4 = 0.870$.

The projection of the structure onto the (010) cell face is shown in Fig. 12; large circles represent thorium, and small, nickel

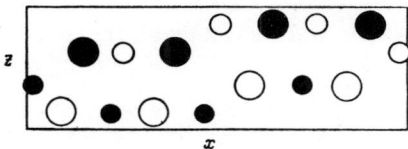

Fig. 12. Projection of the ThNi structure onto the (010) plane, after Florio, Baenziger, and Rundle.
Large and small white circles — Th and Ni atoms with $y = 1/4$; large and small black circles — Th and Ni atoms with $y = 3/4$.

atoms; white corresponds to $y = 0.25$, and black, to $y = 0.75$. The coordination numbers and interatomic distances (in A) are:

Th_I -- $1Th_{II}$ = 3.54 Ni_I -- $2Th_{II}$ = 2.68
     -- $4Th_{II}$ = 3.70   -- $2Th$ = 2.91
     -- $2Th_I$ = 3.78   -- $1Th$ = 3.01
     -- $2Th_{II}$ = 3.79   -- $1Th$ = 3.11
     -- $1Ni$ = 3.01

(cont'd)

Th_I — 1Ni = 3.11 Ni_{II} — 3Th = 2.91
      — 2Ni = 2.91   — 2Th = 2.98
      — 2Ni = 2.98   — 1Th = 3.01
Th_{II} — $1Th_I$ = 3.54   — 1Th = 3.11
      — $4Th_I$ = 3.70   — 2Ni = 2.69
      — $1Th_I$ = 3.79
      — $2Ni_I$ = 2.68
      — 3Ni = 2.91
      — 1Ni = 3.01
      — 1Ni = 3.11

Thorium atoms, like nickel atoms, are of two structural kinds. It is noteworthy that, as in the case of ThCo, against a background of a fairly complex coordination structure of ThNi with total coordination number $\geq$ 12 there are covalent formations; in the present instance, diatomic groups of Th_I — Th_{II} = 3.54 A, and also strong bonds between unlike atoms: Th_{II} — Ni_I = 2.68 A and Th — Ni = 2.91 A.

6. Th_2Ni_{17} type [28]. The structure is hexagonal, with two formula units in the cell. The lattice constants are, for Th_2Ni_{17}: $a=$ 8.37 A; $c=$ 8.14 A; for Pu_2Ni_{17} : $a=$ 8.30 A; $c=$ 8.00 A [60]; for Pu_2Co_{17} : $a=$ 8.325 A; $c=$ 8.104 A [108].

Space group D_{6h}^4 — C6/mmc; atomic coordinates: $2Th_I$ in 2(b); $2Th_{II}$ in 2(d); $6Ni_I$ in 6(g); $12Ni_{II}$ in 12(j), $x=\frac{1}{3}$, $y=$ 0; $12Ni_{III}$ in 12(k), $x=\frac{1}{6}$, $z=$ 0; $4Ni_{IV}$ in 4(f), $z=$ 0.11.

By the nature of the atomic arrangement, Th_2Ni_{17} can be regarded as a superlattice based on the $CaZn_5$ type, with the constant a multiplied by $\sqrt{3}$, and the constant c doubled. $ThNi_5$ has a structure of the $CaZn_5$ type. Fig. 13 shows the projection of the $CaZn_5$, Th_2Ni_{17}, Th_2Fe_{17} and $ThMn_{12}$ structural types onto the (0001) basal plane; their close similarity can be seen. In Fig. 13 small circles represent nickel, zinc, and manganese atoms; large circles containing letters represent thorium and calcium atoms; small white circles lie in the plane of the diagram or are at whole c intervals of the $CaZn_5$ structural type; the small black circles lie 1/2 above or 1/2 below the plane of the white circles; $B_1B_2C_3C_2$ is the cell of the $CaZn_5$ type; $B_1A_3B_4C_3$ is the cell of the Th_2Ni_{17} type, where $c_{Th_2Ni_{17}} \cong 2c_{CaZn_5}$, and the two thorium atoms in the B_2 and B_3 positions, in regular alternation, are held by pairs of Ni_{IV} atoms; $A_2A_3C_3C_2$ is the cell of the $ThMn_{12}$ type, where some of the A(C) and B thorium atoms, in a definite sequence, are replaced by pairs of manganese atoms.

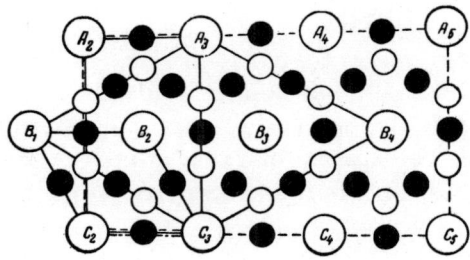

Fig. 13. Projection of $CaZn_5$, Th_2Ni_{17}, Th_2Fe_{17} and $ThMn_{12}$ structural types onto the (0001) plane, after Florio, Baenziger, and Rundle; $B_1B_2C_3C_2$ — $CaZn_5$; $B_1A_3B_4C_3$ — Th_2Ni_{17}; $A_2A_3C_3C_2$ — $ThMn_{12}$; $A_2A_5C_5C_2$ — Th_2Fe_{17}.

Thus, the atomic coordination in the Th_2Ni_{17} structure type in general remains the same as in $CaZn_5$, where coordination number ≥ 12. The heavy atoms are not in mutual contact and are surrounded, at closely similar distances, by eighteen Ni_I, Ni_{II}, and Ni_{III} nickel atoms, and one or two Ni_{IV} atoms. The nickel atoms of the I, II, and III types themselves form a hexagonal close-packed structure, some of the sites in which are occupied by heavy-metal atoms. The interatomic distances have not been calculated [28, 60].

7. Th_2Fe_{17} type [28]. The Th_2Fe_{17} type of structure is a monoclinic variety of the Th_2Ni_{17} type. The cell constants (in Å) are: for Th_2Fe_{17} : $a =$ 9.68; $b =$ 8.56; $c =$ 6.46; $\beta =$ 99°20'; for Th_2Co_{17} : $a =$ 9.62, $b =$ 8.46; $c =$ 6.32; $\beta =$ 99°06'.

Space group C_{2h}^3 -- $C2/m$; atomic coordinates: 4Th in 4(j), $x = \frac{1}{6}$; $z = \frac{1}{3}$; 8Fe$_I$ in 8(j), $x = \frac{1}{6}$, $y_I =$ 0.360, $z_I = \frac{1}{3}$; 8Fe$_{II}$ in 8(j), $x_{II} =$ 0.417, $y_{II} = \frac{1}{4}$; $z_{II} = \frac{1}{3}$; 4Fe$_{III}$ in 4(g), $y_{III} =$ 0.140; 4Fe$_{IV}$ in 4(e); 4Fe$_V$ in 4(i), $x_V = \frac{1}{6}$, $z_V = \frac{2}{3}$; 4Fe$_{VI}$ in 4(i), $x_{VI} =$ 0.416, $z_{VI} =$ 0.147; 2Fe$_{VII}$ in 2(d).

The large rectangle $A_2A_5C_5C_2$ in Fig. 13 represents the projection of the "large" monoclinic cell of the Th_2Fe_{17} type. It is derived from the $CaZn_5$ ($ThFe_5$) type by substitution of thorium atoms by dumb-bell pairs of iron atoms in B_2 positions of the first layer, B_3 positions of the second, and A_3 positions of the third.

The dimensions of the "large" Th_2Fe_{17} cell are so chosen that: $a' =$ 3 $a_{ThFe_5} =$ 14.86 Å; $b' = \sqrt{3}\, a_{ThFe_5} =$ 8.56 Å; $c' =$ 3 $c_{ThFe_5} =$ 12.47 Å; $\beta =$ 90°.

The atomic coordination in Th_2Fe_{17} is in general the same as in Th_2Ni_{17}. The interatomic distances have not been calculated [28].

8. U_6Mn type [27]. The structure is tetragonal, body-centered, with four formula units in the cell. The cell dimensions for isostructural compounds are given in Table 16.

Space group D_{4h}^{18} -- $I4/mcm$; atomic coordinates: 4Mn in 4(a); 16U$_I$ in 16(k) : $x_I =$ 0.2134, $y_I =$ 0.1065; 8U$_{II}$ in 8(h) : $x_{II} =$ 0.4053.

The projection of the U_6Mn structure onto the (001) face is shown in Fig. 14. Large circles represent uranium atoms, and small circles represent atoms of the transition metal. Lines of changing thickness represent height in the Z direction.

TABLE 16

CELL DIMENSIONS FOR ISOSTRUCTURAL COMPOUNDS OF THE U_6Mn TYPE (A)

Compound	a	c	Literature source
U_6Mn	10.29 ± 0.01	5.24 ± 0.02	[27]
U_6Fe	10.31 ± 0.04	5.24 ± 0.02	[27]
U_6Co	10.36 ± 0.02	5.21 ± 0.02	[27]
U_6Ni	10.37 ± 0.04	5.21 ± 0.02	[27]
Pu_6Fe	10.403	5.348	[107, 47]
Pu_6Co	10.46	5.33	[107]

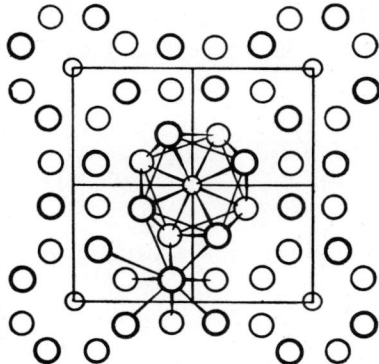

Fig. 14. Projection of the U_6Mn structure onto the (001) plane, after Baenziger, Rundle, Snow, and Wilson.

The coordination numbers and nearest interatomic distances for the average values: a = 10.34 A and c = 5.21 A are:

$$
\begin{aligned}
U_I - 1U_I &= 2.69 \text{ A} & U_{II} - 1U_{II} &= 2.73 \text{ A} \\
- 2Mn &= 2.78 & - 2U_I &= 2.84 \\
- 1U_{II} &= 2.84 & Mn - 2Mn &= 2.61 \text{ A} \\
- 2U_I &= 3.08 & - 8U_I &= 2.78
\end{aligned}
$$

The atomic parameters x and y have not been determined accurately because of difficulty in taking the absorption factor into account. Therefore the coordination and interatomic distances in the U_6Mn structure must be regarded as approximate.

Uranium atoms are of two structural kinds. They form diatomic "molecules": $U_I - U_I$ = 2.69 A and $U_{II} - U_{II}$ = 2.73 A. Here the U -- U distances are even somewhat shorter than the closest distance (2.76 A) in the αU crystal [4]. Moreover, the U_I atom has three strong like and two unlike bonds, and the U_{II} atom has two strong like bonds. Manganese atoms themselves form linear chains penetrating the crystals along the Z axis. At the same time each Mn atom has eight strong bonds (2.78 A) with U_I atoms lying at the corners of a square antiprism twisted at an angle of 51°.

9. UCo type [27]. The structure is cubic, body-centered, with eight formula units in the cell. The lattice constant for UCo is: a = 6.3557 ± 0.0004 A.

Space group $T^5 - I2_13$; atomic coordinates: 8U in 8(a) : x = = 0.0347 ± 0.0015; 8Co in 8(a) : x = 0.294 ± 0.003.

The coordination numbers and interatomic distances (in A) are:

U -- 3U	= 2.772	Co -- 3Co	= 2.677
-- 3U	= 3.645	-- 3Co	= 3.779
-- 1Co	= 2.654	-- 1U	= 2.649
-- 3Co	= 2.809	-- 3U	= 2.809
-- 1Co	= 2.855	-- 1U	= 2.855
-- 3Co	= 2.875	-- 3U	= 2.875

The projection of the UCo structure onto a cube face is shown in Fig. 15. Large circles represent uranium, and small, cobalt atoms. The heights of the atoms in the z direction are indicated by numbers representing fractions of the cell edge.

By the nature of its coordination, the UCo structure type is a deformed structure of the CsCl type. It contains well-defined diatomic "molecules" with U -- Co = 2.65 A, exactly corresponding to the sum of the minimum atomic radius of αU (1.39 A) and the atomic radius of cobalt (1.26 A). In Fig. 15 these UCo "molecules" are shown as dumb-bells. In addition, each uranium atom forms three like bonds U -- U = 2.77 A, corresponding to the minimum interatomic distance in αU (2.78 A), and three strong unlike bonds, U -- Co = 2.81 A.

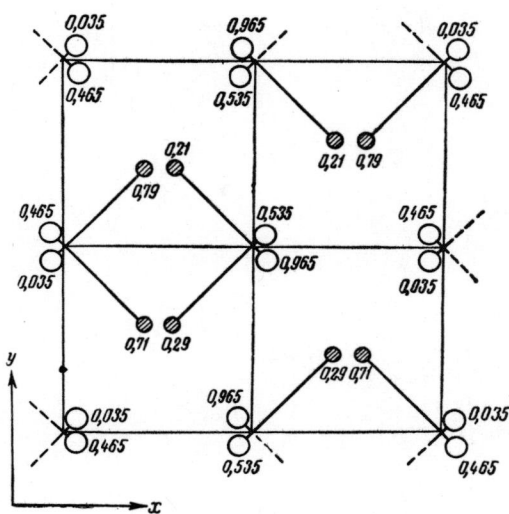

Fig. 15. Projection of the UCo structure onto a cube face.
Large circles – U; small circles – Co; numbers represent height in the Z direction.

It follows from the foregoing that the characteristic crystal-chemical feature of compounds of the actinide metals with metals of the VIIa and VIII subgroups is formation of very close-packed coordination structures, in most cases conforming to the principle: total coordination number $\geqslant$ 12. However, in contrast to the homodesmic structures of the preceding group of systems which includes metals of the IVa, Va, and VIa subgroups, the structures formed in this case are often heterodesmic [59], as on a general background of close packing there are various more or less strong like or unlike atomic bonds, forming either frameworks (the types

TABLE 17

SUBGROUP Ib

	Cu			Ag			Au		
	Formula of compound	Structure type	Lit. source	Formula of compound	Structure type	Lit. source	Formula of compound	Structure type	Lit. source
Th	Th_2Cu $ThCu_2$	$CuAl_2$ AlB_2	[30] [30]	Th_2Ag Th_3Ag_5 $ThAg_3$	$CuAl_2$? ?	[30] [19] [19]	Th_2Au Th_3Au_5 $ThAu_3$	$CuAl_2$? ?	[30] [19] [19]
U	UCu_5	$PdBe_5$	[27]				U_2Au_3 UAu_3	? ?	[32] [32]
Pu	$PuCu$ $PuCu_3$ $PuCu_7$	? ? ?	[108] [108] [108]	$PuAg_3$	?	[60]			
Np									

MgCu$_2$; MgZn$_2$), or layers (the types AlB$_2$; Th$_2$Ni$_{17}$), or chains (the U$_6$Mn type), or diatomic "molecules" (the types UCo; U$_6$Mn; ThNi).

Analysis of the corresponding phase diagrams [19, 20, 23, 47, 62] shows that all the compounds formed in these systems are thermally stable and crystallize either directly from melts or as the result of peritectic reactions. In most cases the compounds are of constant composition, but it should be pointed out that the systems have been studied little in relation to the homogeneity boundaries of the phases of variable composition formed by the compounds in the solid state.

SUBGROUP Ib

It is clear from Table 17 that systems formed by the metals of the copper subgroup with the actinide elements have not been studied fully enough. The crystal structures of a number of compounds have not been determined as yet.

According to the data in Table 17, the known structural types are represented by the following compounds:

CuAl$_2$ type: Th$_2$Cu (a = 7.28 A; c = 5.75 A);
Th$_2$Ag (a = 7.56 A; c = 5.84 A);
Th$_2$Au (a = 7.42 A; c = 5.95 A).

PdBe$_5$ type: UCu$_5$ (a = 7.033—7.038 A; $x = \frac{5}{8}$).

AlB$_2$ type: ThCu$_2$ (a = 4.37 A; c = 3.45 A).

No new structural types have been found. A noteworthy fact is the absence of solubility in the liquid and solid states in the system uranium—silver, analogous to the systems tungsten—silver and chromium—silver.

Formation of the compounds Th$_2$Cu$_{17}$ and U$_2$Cu$_{17}$ should be expected on crystal-chemical grounds, but the phase diagrams for the systems thorium—copper and uranium—copper [62] have not been worked out in sufficient detail for the copper-rich regions.

TABLE 18
SUBGROUP IIb

		Be			Mg			Zn			Cd			Hg	
	Formula of compound	Structure type	Lit. source	Formula of compound	Structure type	Lit. source	Formula of compound	Structure type	Lit. source	Formula of compound	Structure type	Lit. source	Formula of compound	Structure type	Lit. source
Th	ThBe$_{13}$	NaZn$_{13}$	[19] [33]	Th$_x$Mg$_y$ αThMg$_2$ βThMg$_2$	MgNi$_2$ MgCu$_2$	[19] [74] [19] [74]	Th$_{2\pm x}$Zn ThZn$_x$ Th$_x$Zn$_y$ ThZn$_2$ ThZn$_4$ Th$_2$Zn$_{17}$	CuAl$_2$? ? AlB$_2$ BaAl$_4$ Th$_2$Zn$_{17}$	[35] [35] [35] [35] [35] [36]				ThHg$_3$	UHg$_3$	[19]
U	UBe$_{13}$	NaZn$_{13}$	[33]	⊂		[20]	U$_2$Zn$_{17}$	U$_2$Zn$_{17}$	[36]				UHg$_2$ UHg$_3$ UHg$_4$	AlB$_2$ Mg(?) (?)	[37] [37] [37]
Pu	PuBe$_{13}$	NaZn$_{13}$	[21] [47] [60]	Pu$_2$Mg PuMg$_2$		[21] [21]							PuHg$_3$ PuHg$_4$	UHg$_3$ UHg$_4$?	[21] [21]
Np	NpBe$_{13}$	NaZn$_{13}$	[34]												

SUBGROUP IIb

Table 18 contains data on the composition and structure of compounds formed in systems of metals of the IIb subgroup with the actinide elements.

The known structural types are represented by the following compounds:

$MgCu_2$ type:	$\beta ThMg_2$ ($a = 8.570$ A);
$MgNi_2$ type:	$\alpha ThMg_2$ ($a = 6.086$; $c = 19.64$ A);
$NaZn_{13}$ type:	$ThBe_{13}$ ($a = 10.395$ A); UBe_{13} ($a = 10.256$ A); $PuBe_{13}$ ($a = 10.254$ A); $NpBe_{13}$ ($a = 10.266-10.256$ A);
$CuAl_2$ type:	$Th_{2+x}Zn$ ($a = 7.62$ A; $c = 5.62$ A);
AlB_2 type:	$ThZn_2$ ($a = 4.20$ A; $c = 4.17$ A); UHg_2 ($a = 4.99$ A; $c = 3.23$ A);
$BaAl_4$ type:	$ThZn_4$ ($a = 4.26$ A; $c = 10.4$ A).

The $ThHg_3$, UHg_3, and $PuHg_3$ structures are apparently isomorphous [19, 21, 37], but the atomic arrangement, based on hexagonal close packing, is not finally established. Neither has the crystal structure of magnesium–plutonium compounds been determined. Uranium–magnesium alloys give rise to a system with phase separation [20].

Let us consider the new structural types Th_2Zn_{17} and U_2Zn_{17}.

1. Th_2Zn_{17} type [36]. The structure is rhombohedral, with three formula units in the unit cell. The cell dimensions of Th_2Zn_{17} in hexagonal axes are: $a = 9.03$ A; $c = 13.20$ A; $c/a = 1.46$.

Space group D_{3d}^5 — $R\bar{3}m$; atomic coordinates: 6Th in 6(c)$_I$, $z = \frac{1}{3}$; 9Zn$_I$ in 9(d); 18Zn$_{II}$ in 18(f), $x = \frac{1}{3}$; 18Zn$_{III}$ in 18(h), $x = \frac{1}{2}$, $z = \frac{1}{6}$; 6Zn$_{IV}$ in 6(c)$_{II}$, $z = 0.097$.

The atomic arrangement in Th_2Zn_{17}, as in the compounds Th_2Ni_{17}, Th_2Fe_{17} and $ThMn_{12}$ considered above, is based on a structural pattern of the $CaZn_5$ type, and can be described by means of Fig. 13. If $B_1B_2C_3C_2$ is a cell of the $CaZn_5$ type, then $B_1A_3B_4C_3$ is the Th_2Zn_{17} cell, with the period along the Z axis three times the corresponding period for the $CaZn_5$ type of structure; three thorium atoms in the B_2 and B_3 positions, in regular alternation, are bound with pairs of Zn_{IV} atoms in $6(c)_{II}$ sixfold complexes.

It has been suggested [36] that substitution of these complexes by zinc atoms is variable in character; this makes possible the formation of a phase of variable composition, Th_2Zn_{15-17}, which therefore includes the compound $ThZn_8$. If the $6(c)_{II}$ complexes are not occupied by zinc atoms, the crystals have the composition Th_2Zn_{15}; if they are only half occupied by zinc atoms, the composition is $Th_2Zn_{16} = ThZn_8$.

Thus, the atomic coordination in Th_2Zn_{17} is very close to that in Th_2Ni_{17} (see above). The coordination numbers and interatomic distances (in Å) for Th_2Zn_{17} are:

$$\begin{array}{ll}
Th - 6Zn_{II} = 3.01 & Zn_I - 2Th = 3.41 \\
 - 12Zn_{I,III} = 3.41 & - 4Zn_{II} = 2.66 \\
 - 1Zn_{IV} = 3.12 & - 4Zn_{III} = 2.61 \\
 & - 2Zn_{IV} = 2.77 \\
Zn_{II} - 2Th = 3.01 & Zn_{III} - 3Th = 3.41 \\
\phantom{Zn_{II}} - 3Zn_{II} = 3.01 & \phantom{Zn_{III}} - 4Zn_{II} = 2.66 \\
\phantom{Zn_{II}} - 6Zn_{III} = 2.66 & \phantom{Zn_{III}} - 4Zn_{III} = 2.61 \\
\phantom{Zn_{II}} - 2Zn_{IV} = 3.27 & \phantom{Zn_{III}} - 1Zn_{IV} = 2.77 \\
 & Zn_{IV} - 1Th = 3.12 \\
 & \phantom{Zn_{IV}} - 6Zn_{II} = 3.27 \\
 & \phantom{Zn_{IV}} - 6Zn_{III} = 2.77 \\
 & \phantom{Zn_{IV}} - 1Zn_{IV} = 2.56
\end{array}$$

The unit cell of Th_2Zn_{17} is shown in Fig. 16.

2. U_2Zn_{17} type [36]. The structure is hexagonal, with six formula units in the cell. The dimensions of the U_2Zn_{17} cell are:

$a = 8.99$ A; $c = 26.35$ A; $c/a = 2.93$. It is seen that

$$a_{U_2Zn_{17}} \cong a_{Th_2Zn_{17}}; \quad c_{U_2Zn_{17}} \cong 2c_{Th_2Zn_{17}}$$

The U_2Zn_{17} and Th_2Zn_{17} structures are almost identical in the nature of their atomic arrangements. The difference is that because of the existence of a horizontal plane of symmetry the dimensions

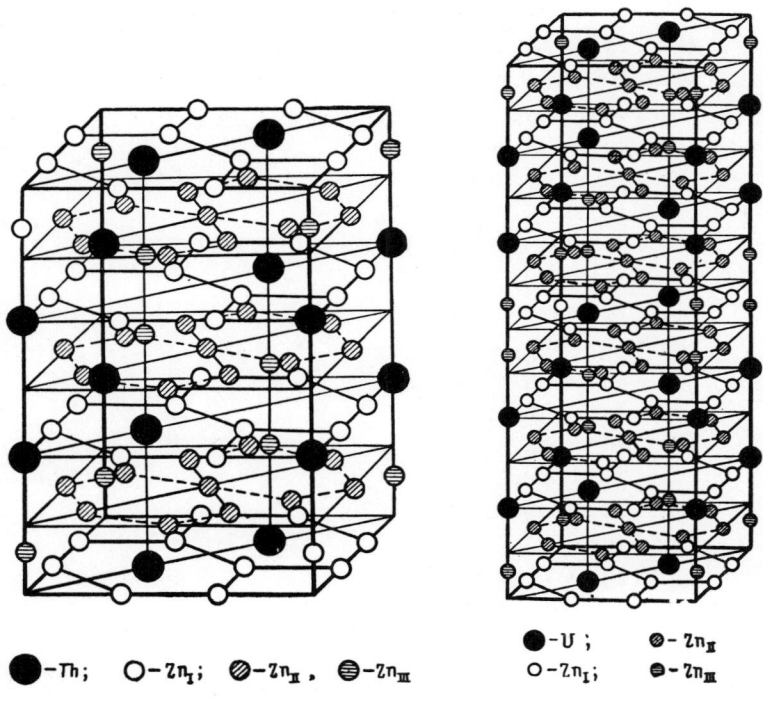

Fig. 16. Unit cell of Th_2Zn_{17}, after Makarov and Vinogradov.

Fig. 17. Unit cell of U_2Zn_{17}, after Makarov and Vinogradov.

of the U_2Zn_{17} cell along the Z axis are double those of the Th_2Zn_{17} cell. This leads to the noncentrosymmetrical space group D_{3h}^1 -- $C\bar{6}m2$ and the following atomic coordinates:

1U	in	1 (c)					
1U	in	1 (d)					
1U	in	1 (e)					
1U	in	1 (f)					
2U	in	2 (g),	$z=$ 1/6				
2U	in	2 (g),	$z=$ 1/3				
2U	in	2 (h),	$z=$ 1/3				
2U	in	2 (i),	$z=$ 1/6				
6Zn	in	6 (l),	$x=$ 1/3,	$y=$ 0			
6Zn	in	6 (m),	$x=$ 1/3,	$y=$ 0			
12Zn	in	12 (o),	$x=$ 1/3,	$y=$ 0,	$z=$ 1/6		
12Zn	in	12 (o),	$x=$ 1/3,	$y=$ 0,	$z=$ 1/3		
6Zn	in	6 (n),	$x=$ 1/2,		$z=$ 1/12		
6Zn	in	6 (n),	$x=$ 1/2,		$z=$ 1/4		
6Zn	in	6 (n),	$x=$ 1/2,		$z=$ 5/12		
6Zn	in	6 (n),	$x=$ 1/6,		$z=$ 1/12		
6Zn	in	6 (n),	$x=$ 1/6,		$z=$ 1/4		
6Zn	in	6 (n),	$x=$ 1/6,		$z=$ 5/12		
6Zn	in	6 (n),	$x=$ 5/6,		$z=$ 1/12		
6Zn	in	6 (n),	$x=$ 5/6,		$z=$ 1/4		
6Zn	in	6 (n),	$x=$ 5/6,		$z=$ 5/12		
2Zn	in	2 (g),			$z=$ 0.049		
2Zn	in	2 (g),			$z=$ 0.451		
2Zn	in	2 (h),			$z=$ 0.118		
2Zn	in	2 (h),			$z=$ 0.784		
2Zn	in	2 (i),			$z=$ 0.284		
2Zn	in	2 (i),			$z=$ 0.618		

As in the previous case, the formation of a phase of variable composition, U_2Zn_{15-17}, is probable.

The coordination and interatomic distances in U_2Zn_{17} are almost the same as in Th_2Zn_{17}, and therefore they are not given here; they will be found in the original paper [36].

The unit cell of U_2Zn_{17} is shown in Fig. 17, which clearly reveals its "two-story" structure as compared with the Th_2Zn_{17} cell in Fig. 16.

TABLE 19
SUBGROUP IIIb

	B			Al			Ga			In			Tl		
	Formula of compound	Structure type	Lit. source	Formula of compound	Structure type	Lit. source	Formula of compound	Structure type	Lit. source	Formula of compound	Structure type	Lit. source	Formula of compound	Structure type	Lit. source
Th	ThB$_4$ ThB$_6$	UB$_4$ CaB$_6$	[38] [39] [1]	ThAl$_3$ ThAl$_3$ Th$_4$Al$_7$ ThAl Th$_3$Al$_2$ Th$_2$Al ThAl$_4$	Ni$_3$Sn AlB$_2$? ThAl U$_3$Si$_2$ CuAl$_2$?	[41] [41] [41] [41] [41] [41] [41]									
U	UB$_2$ UB$_4$ UB$_{12}$	AlB$_2$ UB$_4$ UB$_{12}$	[40] [38] [63]	UAl$_2$ UAl$_3$ UAl$_4$	MgCu$_2$ AuCu$_3$ UAl$_4$	[42] [42] [43] [44]	UGa UGa$_2$ UGa$_3$	UGa AlB$_2$ AuCu$_3$	[46] [46] [43]	UIn$_3$	AuCu$_3$	[43]			
Pu				Pu$_3$Al PuAl$_2$ PuAl$_3$ PuAl$_4$	SrPb$_3$ MgCu$_2$ PuAl$_3$ UAl$_4$	[21] [21,60] [117] [21,60]				Pu$_3$In	AuCu$_3$	[21]			
Np				NpAl$_2$ NpAl$_3$ NpAl$_4$	MgCu$_2$ Cu$_3$Au UAl$_4$	[45] [45] [45]									

SUBGROUP IIIb

The composition of the chemical compounds found in systems of elements of the IIIb subgroup with the actinide metals, and the types of their crystal structure, are given in Table 19.

The known structure types are represented by the following compounds:

$AuCu_3$ type: UAl_3 ($a=$ 4.278 kX); UGa_3 ($a=$ 4.2475 A); UIn_3 ($a=$ 4.6013 A); Pu_3In ($a=$ 4.703 A); $NpAl_3$ ($a=$ 4.262 A).

Ni_3Sn type: $ThAl_3$ ($a=$ 6.500 A; $c=$ 4.626 A; $x=$ 0.854).

$SrPb_3$ type: Pu_3Al ($a=$ 4.499 A; $c=$ 4.538 A).

$MgCu_2$ type: UAl_2 ($a=$ 7.795 kX); $PuAl_{2+x}$ ($a=$ 7.838–7.848 A).

$CuAl_2$ type: Th_2Al ($a=$ 7.62 A; $c=$ 5.86 A).

AlB_2 type: $ThAl_2$ ($a=$ 4.393 A; $c=$ 4.164 A). UGa_2 ($a=$ 4.21 A; $c=$ 4.01 A); UB_2.

CaB_6 type: ThB_6 ($a=$ 4.16 A).

Let us consider the new structural types: UB_4, UB_{12}, ThAl, UGa, UAl_4, $PuAl_3$. The type U_3Si_2, which includes Th_3Al_2, will be described later, with the silicides in subgroup IVb.

1. UB_4 type [38]. The structure is tetragonal, with four formula units in the cell. The lattice constants for ThB_4 are: $a=$ 7.256 A; $c=$ 4.113 A; for UB_4: $a=$ 7.075 A; $c=$ 3.979 A.

Space group D_{4h}^5 — P4/mbm; atomic coordinates: 4Th in 4(g), $u=\frac{5}{16}$; $4B_I$ in 4(e), $v=$ 0.212; $4B_{II}$ in 4(h), $w=$ 0.087; $8B_{III}$ in 8(j), $x=$ 0.170, $y=$ 0.042.

The projection of the UB_4 structure onto the (001) plane is given in Fig. 18.

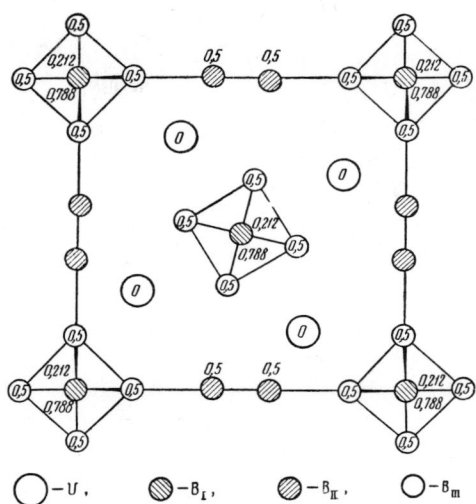

Fig. 18. Projection of the UB$_4$ structure onto the (001) plane; the numbers give the third coordinate; boron octahedrons are marked.

The UB$_4$ structure is a combination of the AlB$_2$ and CaB$_6$ types. Uranium atoms form plane layers in which the close packing characteristic of the AlB$_2$ type breaks down, and in consequence each atom has five nearest like neighbors in a given layer, instead of six. Between these layers there are, first, octahedral voids lying at the centers of tetragonal prisms of eight nearest neighboring uranium atoms, of approximately the same volume as the corresponding voids in the cubic structure of ThB$_6$ of the CaB$_6$ type. The unit cell contains two such voids and they are occupied by octahedrons of B$_I$ and B$_{III}$ atoms in just the same way as in the CaB$_6$ type of structure. Moreover, there are triangular voids in the layers of uranium atoms themselves; these contain B$_{II}$ atoms.

The boron atoms in adjoining voids are in mutual contact and form a continuous spatial network.

The numbers of nearest neighbors and interatomic distances (in A) for UB_4 are:

B_I	— $1B_I$	= 1.69	U —	$4B_I$	= 2.71
	— $4B_{III}$	= 1.69	—	$4B_{II}$	= 2.87
B_{II}	— $1B_{II}$	= 1.74	—	$2B_{II}$	= 3.01
	— $2B_{III}$	= 1.75	—	$8B_{III}$	= 2.76
B_{III}	— $2B_I$	= 1.69	—	$4U$	= 3.65
	— $1B_{II}$	= 1.75	—	$1U$	= 3.75
	— $2B_{III}$	= 1.75	—	$2U$	= 3.98

Thus, each uranium atom in UB_4 has five strong $U - U \simeq 3.7$ A bonds. All the U — B interatomic distances are considerably greater than the sum of the maximum radii of uranium and boron (1.52 + 0.91 = 2.43 A), indicating that this bond is weak. On the other hand, all the B — B bonds are less than double the radius of the boron atom (1.82 A); this indicates that these bonds are covalent. Each B_I atom has five strong B — B = 1.69 A bonds, and the B_{II} atoms have three each; the B_{III} atom has five neighboring boron atoms at somewhat different distances.

Therefore the U — U and B — B interatomic bonds are predominant in crystals of UB_4, as is the case in Laves phases ($MgCu_2$, $MgZn_2$, and $MgNi_2$). This shows that UB_4 crystals are heterodesmic.

2. UB_{12} type [63]. The structure is cubic, face-centered, with four formula units in the cell. The lattice constant $a = 7.473$ A.

Space group O_h^5 — Fm3m; atomic coordinates: 4U in 4(a); 48B in 48(i), $x = \frac{1}{6}$.

The projection of the UB_{12} structure onto the face of a cubic unit cell is shown in Fig. 19.

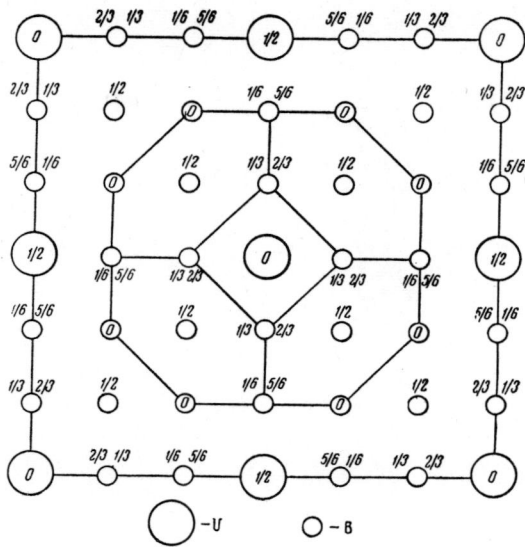

Fig. 19. Projection of the UB_{12} structure onto the face of a cubic unit cell; the numbers represent the third coordinate; the cubic octahedron of B atoms around the U atom is shown.

The boron atoms form a three-dimensional framework, with uranium atoms distributed in its voids at long distances (U — U = = 5.28 A) in a face-centered cube pattern. The uranium atoms are situated at centers of Fedorov cubic octahedrons consisting of boron atoms. Therefore each uranium atom is surrounded by 24 boron atoms at a distance of 2.79 A, which is greater than the sum of the maximum atomic radius of uranium (1.52 A) and the radius of the boron atom (0.91 A). Each boron atom forms five strong B — B = 1.76 A bonds with its five nearest neighbors; these bonds are somewhat shorter than double the radius of the boron atom (1.82 A). These five covalent boron bonds in UB_{12}, and the analogous bonds in UB_4, are in good agreement with the well-known (8—N) Hume-Rothery rule for structures of elements of the b subgroups.

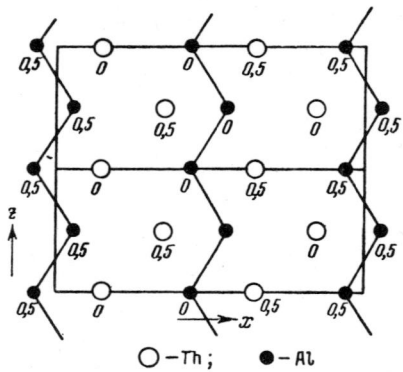

Fig. 20. Projection of the ThAl structure onto the (XOZ) plane.
White circles — Th atoms; black circles — Al atoms; numbers indicate heights in the y direction.

3. ThAl type [41]. The structure is rhombic, with four formula units in the unit cell. The lattice constants are: $a = 11.45$ A; $b = 4.42$ A; $c = 4.19$ A.

Space group D_2^5 — $C222_1$; atomic coordinates: 4Th in 4(a), $x_1 = 0.147$; 4Al in 4(a), $x_2 = 0.443$. The projection of the ThAl structure onto the $x0z$ plane is shown in Fig. 20 for two unit cells.

The numbers of neighboring atoms and interatomic distances (in A) are:

$$\begin{array}{ll} \text{Th} - 6\text{Al} = 3.22 & \text{Al} - 2\text{Al} = 2.46 \\ \phantom{\text{Th}} - 1\text{Al} = 3.39 & \phantom{\text{Al}} - 6\text{Th} = 3.22 \\ \phantom{\text{Th}} - 4\text{Th} = 3.85 & \phantom{\text{Al}} - 1\text{Th} = 3.39 \\ \phantom{\text{Th}} - 2\text{Th} = 3.96 & \end{array}$$

A characteristic feature of this heterodesmic structure is the presence of infinite broken chains of aluminum atoms with very short and therefore strong Al—Al = 2.46 A bonds. These chains penetrate the crystals in the direction of the Z axis, as Fig. 20 shows. Each aluminum atom has, in addition to the Al--Al bonds in the chains, six Al--Th = 3.22 A bonds, the length of which is equal to the sum of the atomic radii of thorium and aluminum. The thorium atoms are not in mutual contact, but each has six neighbors--Al atoms--at a distance of 3.22 A.

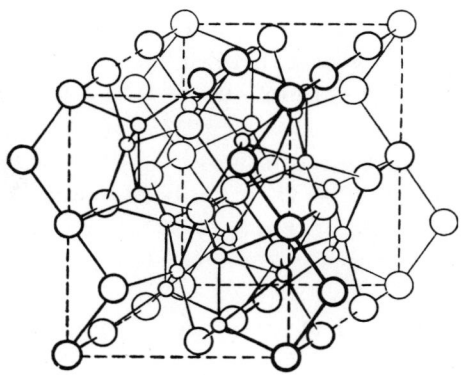

Fig. 21. Unit cell of UGa, after Makarov and Levdik.
Large circles – U atoms; small circles – Ga atoms.

4. UGa type [46]. The structure is rhombic, with 16 formula units in the unit cell. The lattice constants for UGa are: a = 9.40 A; b = 7.60 A; c = 9.42 A.

Space group D_{2h}^{17} -- Cmcm; atomic coordinates: $4U_I$ in 4(a); $4U_{II}$ in 4(c) : y = 0.212; $8U_{III}$ in 8(e) : x = 0.300; $8Ga_I$ in 8(f) : y = 0.689, z = 0.118; $8Ga_{II}$ in 8(g) : x = 0.260, y = 0.354.

The unit cell of UGa is shown in Fig. 21.

The coordination numbers and nearest interatomic distances (in A) are:

$$
\begin{aligned}
U_I &\;-\; 2U_{III} = 2.82 & Ga_I &\;-\; 1Ga_I = 2.48\\
&\;-\; 2U_{II} = 2.85 & &\;-\; 2Ga_{II} = 2.86\\
&\;-\; 2Ga_I = 2.61 & &\;-\; 2U_I = 2.61\\
U_{II} &\;-\; 2Ga_{II} = 2.66 & &\;-\; 2U_{III} = 2.605\\
U_{III} &\;-\; 2Ga_I = 2.605 & Ga_{II} &\;-\; 2Ga_I = 2.86\\
&\;-\; 2Ga_{II} = 2.66 & &\;-\; 2U_{II} = 2.6\\
& & &\;-\; 2U_{III} = 2.66
\end{aligned}
$$

The heterodesmic character of the UGa structure is manifested in the formation of infinite broken chains of $U_I - U_{II}$ atoms with bond length 2.85 A, characteristic of αU, of two other strong bonds $U_I - U_{III} = 2.82$ A, and also of "molecules" of $Ga_I - Ga_I = 2.48$ A, present in the structure of metallic gallium with almost the same bond length, 2.45 A. The U — Ga bonds correspond to the sum of the minimum radii of uranium (1.38 A) and gallium (1.23 A); this fact is indicative of the high strength of these bonds.

5. UAl_4 type [44]. The structure is rhombic, with four formula units in the unit cell. The three isostructural compounds have the following lattice constants (in A):

	a	b	c
UAl_4 [44]	4.41	6.27	13.71
$NpAl_4$ [45]	4.42	6.26	13.71
$PuAl_4$ [60]	4.42	6.26	13.66

Space group D_{2h}^{28} — Imma; atomic coordinates: 4Pu in 4(e), $z = 0.111$; $4Al_I$ in 4(e), $z = -0.111$; $4Al_{II}$ in 4(b); $8Al_{III}$ in 8(h), $y = -0.033$, $z = 0.314$.

The projection of the UAl_4 structure onto the $0yz$ plane is shown in Fig. 22. Coordination around the uranium atom is shown by heavy lines. The numbers near the circles represent the third coordinate.

The coordination numbers and interatomic distances in (A) for $PuAl_4$ [60] are:

Pu — 4Al$_{III}$ = 3.01   Al$_{II}$ — 4Pu = 3.11
— 1Al$_{I}$ = 3.03   — 2Al$_{III}$ = 2.5
— 4Al$_{II}$ = 3.11   — 4Al$_{I}$ = 3.1
— 2Al$_{I}$ = 3.13   — 2Al$_{II}$ = 3.13
— 2Al$_{III}$ = 3.29
Al$_{1}$ — 1Pu = 3.03   Al$_{III}$ — 2Pu = 3.01
— 2Pu = 3.13   — 1Pu = 3.29
— 4Al$_{III}$ = 2.79   — 1Al$_{II}$ = 2.55
— 2Al$_{III}$ = 3.09   — 1Al$_{III}$ = 2.72
— 4Al$_{II}$ = 3.11   — 2Al$_{III}$ = 2.79
                               — 2Al$_{III}$ = 2.82
                               — 1Al$_{I}$ = 3.09
                               — 1Al$_{III}$ = 3.54

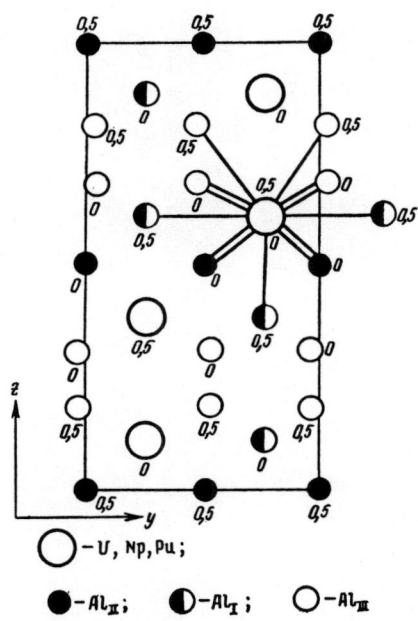

○ — U, Np, Pu;
● — Al$_{II}$;   ◐ — Al$_{I}$;   ○ — Al$_{III}$

Fig. 22. Projection of the UAl$_4$ structure onto the (Oyz) plane.
Coordination around U is shown; the numbers indicate heights in the x direction.

The plutonium atoms are not in mutual contact but are surrounded, at somewhat different distances, by 13 aluminum atoms; five of these are at the closest distance Pu -- Al = 3.01--3.03 A, which exactly corresponds to the sum of the atomic radii of γplutonium (1.60 A) and aluminum (1.43 A). The aluminum atoms are of three structural kinds, each of which has rather complex coordination. Al_I has four strong bonds of the type Al_I -- Al_{III} = = 2.79 A < $2R_{Al}$ = 2.86 A; Al_{II} has two of the strongest bonds, Al_{II} -- Al_{III} = 2.55 A; Al_{III} has six strong Al -- Al bonds with lengths varying from 2.55 to 2.82 A.

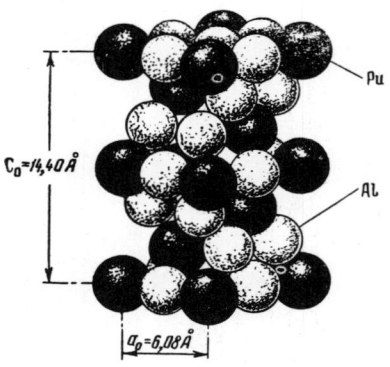

Fig. 23. Unit cell of $PuAl_3$, after Runnalls.

6. $PuAl_3$ type [60, 107, 117]. The structure is hexagonal, with six formula units in the unit cell. The lattice constants of $PuAl_3$ are: a = 6.10 ± 0.02; c = 14.47 ± 0.04 A.

The $PuAl_3$ structure is closely allied in the character of its atomic coordination to the cubic $AuCu_3$ structural type, which is the crystal form of an analog of $PuAl_3$ -- UAl_3. The cubic face-centered structure of the $AuCu_3$ type is one of the simplest ordered structures with close cubic packing, in which the close-packed layers of atoms are superposed on each other in the sequence ... ABCABC ...

It has been found [60] that in the PuAl$_3$ structure the close-packed layers are in the following sequence: ... ABCACB ... The consequent transition to hexagonal symmetry, with P$\bar{6}$m2 or P6$_3$/mmc as possible space groups, allows of certain displacements of the atoms from the ideal positions; these do in fact occur in PuAl$_3$.

On the basis of the model proposed by Runnalls [60], Larson and Cromer [107, 117] found the following atomic coordinates for PuAl$_3$: D_{6h}^4 — P6$_3$/mmc. 2Pu in 2(b); 4Pu in 4(f), $z = $ 0.0892 ± 0.0001; 6Al in 6(h), $x = $ 0.5160 ± 0.0030; 12Al in 12(k), $x = $ 0.8336 ± 0.0040; $z = $ 0.0815 ± 0.0006.

The PuAl$_3$ unit cell is shown in perspective in Fig. 23.

SUBGROUP IVb

The compositions and structural types of the chemical compounds formed in systems of elements of subgroup IVb with the actinide metals are given in Table 20.

The known structural types are represented by the following compounds:

- AuCu$_3$ type: USi$_3$ ($a = $ 4.0353 A); UGe$_3$ ($a = $ 4.2062 A); USn$_3$ ($a = $ 4.626 A); UPb$_3$ ($a = $ 4.7834 A); ThPb$_3$; PuGe$_3$ ($a = $ 4.223 A); PuSn$_3$ ($a = $ 4.630 A); PuPb$_3$ ($a = $ 4.808 A).

- AlB$_2$ type: βUSi$_2$ ($a = $ 3.85 kX; $c = $ 4.06 kX); βPuSi$_2$ ($a = $ 3.884 A; $c = $ 4.082 A); βThSi$_2$ ($a = $ 3.986 A; $c = $ 4.227 A).

- ThSi$_2$ type: αThSi$_2$ ($a = $ 4.126 A; $c = $ 14.346 A; $z = $ 0.417); αUSi$_2$ ($a = $ 3.97 A; $c = $ 13.71 A); αPuSi$_2$ ($a = $ 3.97 A; $c = $ 13.55 A); αNpSi$_2$ ($a = $ 3.96 A; $c = $ 13.67 A); αPuGe$_2$ ($a = $ 4.102 A; $c = $ 13.81 A).

FeB type: USi ($a = 5.65$ kX; $b = 7.65$ kX; $c = 3.90$ kX; $x_U = 0.125$; $y_U = 0.180$; $x_{Si} = 0.611$; $y_{Si} = 0.028$).
PuSi ($a = 5.727$ A; $b = 7.933$ A; $c = 3.847$ A).

CaC$_2$ type: UC$_2$ ($a = 3.517$ A; $c = 5.987$ A); (phase of variable composition UC$_{1.35 \to 2.3}$, $a = 3.535-3.512$ A; $c = 5.970-5.968$ A).

NaCl type: ThC$_{n1 \to n2}$ ($a = 5.29-5.34$ A); UC ($a = 4.951$ A); NpC; PuC ($a = 4.910$ A).

It is interesting to note that in the system thorium--carbon [62] at temperatures above 1600° a very extensive region of solid solutions of carbon in thorium, ThC$_{0 \to 2}$, is formed, extending to the composition ThC$_2$. The compound ThC is formed at lower temperatures and has variable composition, the limits of which have not been precisely determined. The crystal structure of the high-temperatures region ThC$_{0 \to 2}$ has not been established.

Let us consider the new structural types: U$_3$Si$_2$; U$_3$Si; Pu$_2$C$_3$ and ThC$_2$.

1. U$_3$Si$_2$ type [64]. The structure is tetragonal, with two formula units in the unit cell. The lattice constants for U$_3$Si$_2$: $a = 7.3151$ kX; $c = 3.8925$ kX; for Th$_3$Si$_2$: $a = 7.841$ A; $c = 4.166$ A.

Space group D_{4h}^5 -- P4/mbm; atomic coordinates 2U$_I$ in 2(a); 4U$_{II}$ in 4(h), $u = 0.181$; 4Si in 4(g), $v = 0.389$.

The projection of the U$_3$Si$_2$ structure along the four-fold axis is given in Fig. 24.

The coordination numbers and interatomic distances (in A) are:

$$
\begin{array}{llll}
U_I & - 4Si & = 2.96 & Si - 1Si = 2.30 \\
 & - 8U_{II} & = 3.32 & - 2U_{II} = 2.90 \\
U_{II} & - 2Si & = 2.90 & - 4U_{II} = 2.93 \\
 & - 4Si & = 2.93 & - 2U_I = 2.96 \\
 & - 4U_I & = 3.32 & \\
\end{array}
$$

TABLE 20

SUBGROUP IVb

	C			Si			Ge			Sn			Pb		
	Formula of compound	Structure type	Lit. source	Formula of compound	Structure type	Lit. source	Formula of compound	Structure type	Lit. source	Formula of compound	Structure type	Lit. source	Formula of compound	Structure type	Lit. source
Th	$ThC_{0\to 2}$ ($t>1600°C$) ThC_2	NaCl (для ThC) $\overline{ThC_2}$	[19] [66]	$\alpha ThSi_2$ $\beta ThSi_2$ Th_3Si_2	$\alpha ThSi_2$ AlB_2 U_3Si_2	[19] [48] [19] [19]							$ThPb_3$	$AuCu_3$	[19]
U	UC U_2C_3 UC_2	NaCl Pu_2C_3 CaC_2	[1] [65] [1]	U_3Si U_3Si_2 USi αUSi_2 βUSi_2 USi_3	$\underline{U_3Si}$ $\underline{U_3Si_2}$ FeB $ThSi_2$ AlB_2 $AuCu_3$	[1;64] [1;64] [1;64] [1;64] [1;64] [43]	UGe_3	$AuCu_3$	[43]	USn_3	$AuCu_3$	[43]	UPb UPb_3	$AuCu_3$	[43] [43]
Pu	PuC Pu_2C_3	NaCl $\overline{Pu_2C_3}$	[21] [65]	PuSi $\alpha PuSi_2$ $\beta PuSi_2$	FeB $\alpha TiSi_2$ AlB_2	[21] [21] [49]	Pu_2Ge_2 $PuGe_2$ $PuGe_3$	$\alpha ThSi_2$ $AuCu_3$	[21] [21] [21]	$PuSn_3$	$AuCu_3$	[21]	Pu_2Pb $PuPb_3$	$AuCu_3$	[47] [21] [47]
Np	NpC Np_2C_3 NpC_2	NaCl Pu_2C_3? CaC_2?	[1] [1] [1]	$NpSi_2$	$ThSi_2$	[1]									

89

The uranium atoms are not in close mutual contact. The U — Si interatomic distances are somewhat greater than the sum of the maximum radius of uranium (1.52 A) and of silicon (1.34 A). Silicon atoms form well-defined diatomic Si_2 molecules with strong short Si — Si = 2.30 A bonds.

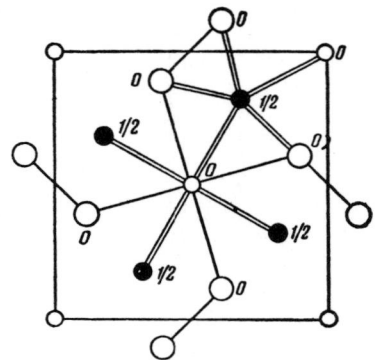

Fig. 24. Projection of the U_3Si_2 structure onto the (001) plane, after Zachariasen.
Large white circles — Si atoms; small white circles — U_I atoms; small black circles — U_{II} atoms.

2. U_3Si type [64]. The structure is body-centered, tetragonal, with four formula units in the unit cell.

Lattice constants for U_3Si : a= 6.017 kX, c = 8.679 kX.

Space group D_{4h}^{18} — J4/mcm; atomic coordinates: $4U_I$ in 4(a); $8U_{II}$ in 8(h), u = 0.231 · 4Si in 4(b).

The projection of the U_3Si structure along the four-fold axis is shown in Fig. 25.

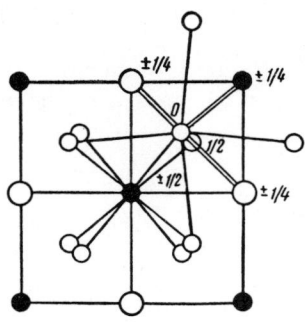

Fig. 25. Projection of the U_3Si structure onto the (001) plane, after Zachariasen.
Large white circles — Si atoms; small black circles — U_I atoms; small white circles — U_{II} atoms.

The coordination numbers and interatomic distances (in A) are:

U_I — 4Si = 3.01   Si — $4U_I$ = 3.01
    — $8U_{II}$ = 3.04   — $4U_{II}$ = 2.92
U_{II} — 2Si = 2.92   — $4U_{II}$ = 3.17
    — 2Si = 3.17
    — $4U_I$ = 3.04
    — $4U_{II}$ = 3.02

In contrast to other silicides, U_3Si does not contain bonds between silicon atoms. Each silicon atom is surrounded, at similar distances, by 12 uranium atoms, the nearest of which are four Si — U_{II} = 2.92 A bonds, but all these distances are greater than the sum of the maximum atomic radii of uranium (1.52 A) and silicon (1.34 A). Each uranium atom forms eight bonds of the type U — U = 3.02—3.04 A, exactly corresponding to the maximum atomic diameter of αU (3.04 A).

The U_3Si type of structure may be regarded as a distorted structure of the Cu_3Au type. If the U_{II} atoms were displaced so that $u = \frac{1}{4}$, and at the same time the ratio of the axes was lowered from 1.442 to $\sqrt{2}$, U_3Si would have a structure of the Cu_3Au type.

3. Pu_2C_3 type [65]. The structure is cubic, body-centered, with eight formula units in the unit cell. The lattice constant for Pu_2C_3: $a = 8.129$ A.

Space group $T_d^6 - J\bar{4}3d$; atomic coordinates: 16Pu in 16(c), $x_{Pu} = 0.050$; 24C in 24(d), $x_C = 0.280$.

The projection of the Pu_2C_3 structure onto the face of a cube is shown in Fig. 26.

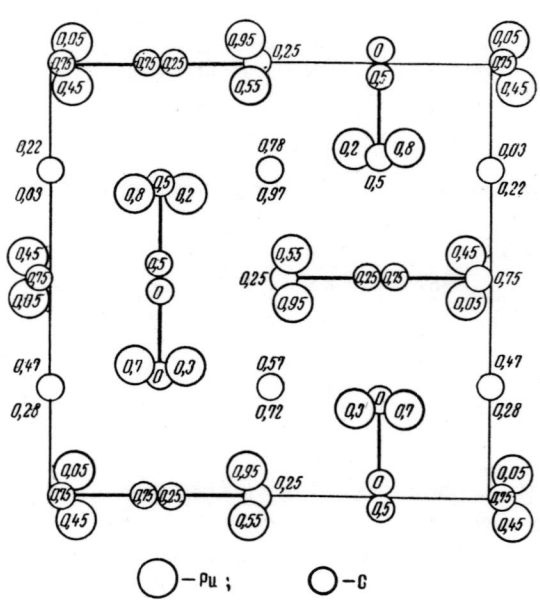

Fig. 26. Projection of the Pu_2C_3 structure onto the face of a cube. Dumb-bell molecules of C_2 are shown.

The coordination numbers and interatomic distances (in A) are:

$$
\begin{array}{llll}
\text{Pu} - & 3\text{Pu} = 3.35 & \text{C} - & 1\text{C} = 1.54 \\
- & 2\text{Pu} = 3.52 & - & 2\text{Pu} = 2.48 \\
- & 6\text{Pu} = 3.70 & - & 2\text{Pu} = 2.51 \\
- & 3\text{C} = 2.48 & - & 2\text{Pu} = 2.84 \\
- & 3\text{C} = 2.51 & & \\
- & 3\text{C} = 2.84 & & \\
\end{array}
$$

Carbon atoms form C_2 molecules with C -- C bonds 1.54 A long. The plutonium atoms are not in close mutual contact if the atomic radius of plutonium is taken to be 1.60 A (see p. 40). Each plutonium atom has six carbon atoms as nearest neighbors at distances of 2.48--2.51 A. Each carbon atom, apart from its like neighbor in the C_2 molecules, has four neighboring plutonium atoms at a distance of 2.48--2.51 A.

4. ThC_2 type [66]. The structure is monoclinic, with four formula units in the unit cell. The lattice constants for ThC_2: $a = 6.53$ A; $b = 4.24$ A; $c = 6.56$ A; $\beta = 104°$.

The space group and atomic coordinates have been determined by neutron diffraction: C_{2h}^6 -- C2/c; 4Th in 4(e), $y = 0.202$: 8C in 8(f), $x = 0.290$, $y = 0.132$, $z = 0.082$.

The ThC_2 unit cell is represented in Fig. 27, where the dash lines also indicate the pseudotetragonal ThC_2 cell found earlier by Stackelberg [82].

The coordination numbers and interatomic distances (in A) for ThC_2 are:

$$
\begin{array}{llll}
\text{C} - & 1\text{C} = 1.47 & \text{Th} - & 2\text{Th} = 3.70 \\
\text{Th} - & 2\text{C} = 2.43 & - & 4\text{Th} = 3.90 \\
- & 2\text{C} = 2.38 & - & 2\text{Th} = 4.14 \\
- & 2\text{C} = 2.92 & & \\
- & 2\text{C} = 2.89 & & \\
- & 2\text{C} = 2.86 & & \\
\end{array}
$$

Carbon atoms form C_2 molecules with C -- C bonds 1.47 A long; this excludes the possibility of the C_2 groups being acetylenic in character, as in that case the length of the triple C -- C bond

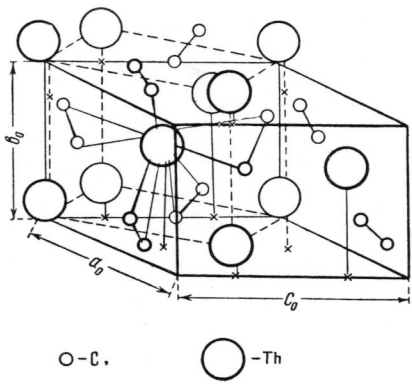

Fig. 27. The ThC_2 unit cell, after Hunt and Rundle.

should be 1.2 A. Each C_2 group is surrounded by six thorium atoms. Each thorium atom has four carbon atoms as nearest neighbors at distances of 2.38--2.43 A, which corresponds closely to the sum of univalent covalent radii of thorium and carbon (2.42 A), according to L. Pauling [6]. The thorium atoms are apparently not in mutual contact.

SUBGROUPS Vb, VIb

The compositions and structural types of the compounds formed by elements of the Vb and VIb subgroups with the actinide metals are given in Tables 21 and 22.

The known structural types are represented by the following compounds:

NaCl type: ThN; UN (a= 4.88 A); PuN (a= 4.895 kX); NpN (a= 4.887 kX); $ThP_{0.75}$ (a= 5.818 A); UP; PuP (a= 5.664 A); ThAs (a= 5.960 kX); UAs (a= 5.767 A); PuAs (a = 5.855 A);

NaCl cont'd: Usb (a= 6.191 kX); PuBi (a= 6.350 A); ThSe (a= 5.863 kX); USe (a= 5.739 kX); UTe (a= 6.151 kX); PuTe (a= 6.183 A); UO (a= 4.92 A); PuO (a= 4.948 kX); NpO (a= 5.00 kX); ThS (a= 5.682 A); US (a= 5.473 kX); 'PuS (a= 5.525 kX).

CsCl type: ThTe (a= 3.819 kX).

Th_3P_4 type: Th_3P_4 (a= 8.600 A); Np_3P_4; U_3P_4 (a= 8.197 A); Th_3As_4 (a= 8.825 kX); U_3As_4 (a= 8.507 A); U_3Sb_4; U_3Te_4 (a= 9.378 kX); $PuS_{1.33 \to 1.50}$ (a= 8.437 kX).

Cu_2Sb type: $ThAs_2$ (a = 4.078 kX; c= 8.558 kX; x_{As}= 0.64; x_{Th}= 0.28); UAs_2 (a= 3.954 A; c= 8.116 A); USb_2 (a= 4.272 A; c= 8.741 A); UP_2 (a= 3.800 A; c= 7.762 A).

Sb_2S_3 type: Th_2S_3 (a= 10.97 kX; b= 10.83 kX; c= 3.95 kX); Th_2Se_3 (a= 11.34 A; b= 11.57 A; c= 4.27 A); U_2S_3 (a= 10.39 kX; b= 10.63 kX; c= 3.88 kX); Np_2S_3 (a= 10.3 kX; b= 10.6 kX; c= 3.85 kX).

$PbCl_2$ type: ThS_2 (a= 4.268 A; b= 7.264 A; c= 8.617 A); βUS_2 (a= 4.12 A; b= 7.11 A; c= 8.46 A); $ThSe_2$ (a= 4.420 A; b= 7.610 A; c= 9.064 A).

CaF_2 type: ThO_2 (a= 5.59 A); UO_2 (a= 5.458 A); PuO_2 (a= 5.396 A); NpO_2 (a= 5.425 A); UN_2 (a= 5.31 A).

Mn_2O_3 type: U_2N_3 (a= 10.678 A); Pu_2O_3 (a = 11.04 A).

La_2O_3 type: βPu_2O_3 (a= 3.841; c= 5.958 A); Th_2N_3 (a= 3.875; c= 6.175 A).

Many of these compounds are phases of variable composition, but their homogeneity regions have not been studied.

The following compounds of variable composition have been studied most fully:

TABLE 21

SUBGROUP Vb

	N			P			As			Sb			Bi		
	Formula of compound	Structure type	Lit. source	Formula of compound	Structure type	Lit. source	Formula of compound	Structure type	Lit. source	Formula of compound	Structure type	Lit. source	Formula of compound	Structure type	Lit. source
Th	ThN Th$_2$N$_3$	NaCl La$_2$O$_3$	[1] [1]	ThP$_{0.75}$ Th$_3$P$_4$	NaCl Th$_3$P$_4$	[1] [82]	ThAs Th$_3$As$_4$ ThAs$_2$	NaCl Th$_3$P$_4$ Cu$_2$Sb	[50] [50] [50]				Th$_2$Bi Th$_3$Bi$_5$		[19] [19]
U	UN UN$_{1.5-2.0}$	NaCl Mn$_2$O$_3$—CaF$_2$	[81] [81]	UP U$_3$P$_4$ UP$_2$	NaCl Th$_3$P$_4$ Cu$_2$Sb	[83] [83] [84]	U$_2$As UAs U$_3$As$_4$ UAs$_2$	? NaCl Th$_3$P$_4$ Cu$_2$Sb	[51] [51, 52] [52] [52]	USb U$_3$Sb$_4$ USb$_2$	NaCl Th$_3$P$_4$ Cu$_2$Sb	[53] [53] [53]	UBi U$_3$Bi$_4$ UBi$_2$	? ? ?	[53, 111] [53, 111] [53, 111]
Pu	PuN	NaCl	[67]	PuP	NaCl	[21]	PuAs	NaCl	[21]				PuBi	NaCl	[21]
Np	NpN	NaCl	[67]	Np$_3$P$_4$	Th$_3$P$_4$	[1]									

TABLE 22

SUBGROUP VIb

	O Formula of compound	O Structure type	O Lit. source	S Formula of compound	S Structure type	S Lit. source	Se Formula of compound	Se Structure type	Se Lit. source	Te Formula of compound	Te Structure type	Te Lit. source	Po Formula of compound	Po Structure type	Po Lit. source
Th	ThO$_2$	CaF$_2$	[1]	ThS Th$_2$S$_3$ Th$_7$S$_{12}$ ThS$_2$	NaCl Sb$_2$S$_3$ Th$_7$S$_{12}$ PbCl$_2$	[19, 78] [19, 78] [77] [19, 78]	ThSe Th$_2$Se$_3$ Th$_7$Se$_{12}$ ThSe$_2$	NaCl Sb$_2$S$_3$ Th$_7$S$_{12}$ PbCl$_2$	[54] [54] [54] [54]	ThTe	CsCl	[56]			
U	UO UO$_{2\rightarrow 2,4}$ UO$_{2,56\rightarrow 3,0}$ αUO$_3$	NaCl CaF$_2$ αβγδ? αUO$_3$	[81] [76, 81] [76, 81] [69]	US U$_2$S$_3$ αUS$_2$ βUS$_2$ γUS$_2$	NaCl Sb$_2$S$_3$ PbCl$_2$	[78] [78] [79] [79] [79]	USe USe$_2$	NaCl	[55] [51]	UTe U$_3$Te$_4$ U$_2$Te$_3$ UTe$_2$	NaCl Th$_3$P$_4$	[55] [55] [51] [55]			
Pu	PuO Pu$_2$O$_3$ PuO$_{1,5\rightarrow 1,75}$ PuO$_2$	NaCl La$_2$O$_3$ Mn$_2$O$_3$ CaF$_2$	[21] [21] [21] [21]	PuS PuS$_{1,33\rightarrow 1,50}$	NaCl Th$_3$P$_4$	[78] [80]				PuTe	NaCl	[21]			
Np	NpO Np$_3$O$_8$ NpO$_2$	NaCl CaF$_2$	[1] [1] [1]	Np$_2$S$_8$	Sb$_2$S$_3$	[78]									

$UN_{1.5 \to 2.0}$ [81]. Within the homogeneity region of this compound there is a continuous transition from a structure of the Mn_2O_3 type (for $UN_{1.5} = U_2N_3$) to a structure of the CaF_2 type (for UN_2). This type of structural change also includes $PuO_{1.50 \to 1.75}$ [21].

$PuS_{1.33 \to 1.50}$ [80]. The compound of the composition $PuS_{1.33} = Pu_3S_4$ has a structure of the Th_3P_4 type. As the sulfur content of the $PuS_{1.33 \to 1.50}$ phase increases, there is a gradual subtraction of plutonium atoms, and at the composition $Pu_{1.50} = Pu_2S_3$ the 12(a) positions statistically contain 10 2/3 plutonium atoms instead of the 12 for Pu_3S_4. Thus, Pu_2S_3 has a defect structure of the Th_3P_4 type.

$UO_{2.0 \to 2.4}$ [76, 81]. As the oxygen content increases there is a gradual transition from a cubic structure of the CaF_2 type (for UO_2) to a tetragonal $UO_{2.4}$ structure, details of the atomic arrangement in which have not been determined.

$UO_{2.56 \to 3.0}$ [76]. The crystal structure of these oxides has not been established. The oxide UO_3 has several polymorphic modifications, the stability temperature ranges of which have not been determined precisely. The crystal structure of one modification of UO_3 has been determined by Zachariasen [69]. It has been reported [110] that the oxide with the composition $UO_{2.82}$ has a cubic structure of the ReO_3 type with vacancies in the cationic part of the lattice, and has lattice constant $a = 4.146$ A.

Data on the structure of uranium–bismuth compounds are contradictory. According to R. Ferro [53], the compound UBi has a structure of the NaCl type ($a = 6.364$ kX), the compound U_3Bi_4, a structure of the Th_3P_4 type ($a = 9.350$ kX), and the compound UBi_2, a structure of the Cu_2Sb type. However, according to the results of careful neutron-diffraction phase analysis performed by R. Teitel [111], UBi has a tetragonal ($a = 11.12$ A; $c = 10.55$ A) body-centered structure with 48 atoms in the cell, the coordinates of which have not been established; the compound UBi_2 has cubic structure ($a = 8.89$ A) with 24 atoms in the cell. It is probable that UBi_2 has structure of the $MgCu_2$ type. Teitel did not determine the U_3Bi_4 cell.

Let us consider the new structural types: Th_7S_{12} and αUO_3.

1. Th_7S_{12} type [77]. The compound of variable composition $ThS_{1.71 \to 1.76}$ includes Th_7S_{12}, which has a hexagonal structure with one formula unit in the unit cell. Lattice constants for Th_7S_{12}: $a = 11.041$ kX; $c = 3.983$ kX; for Th_7Se_{12}: $a = 11.569$ A; $c = 4.23$ A.

Space group $C_{6h}^2 - C6_3/m$; atomic coordinates: $1Th_I$ in 2(a) (statistical); $6Th_{II}$ in 6(h) : $x_{Th} = 0.513$, $y_{Th} = -0.283$; $6S_I$ in 6(h) : $x_{S_I} = 0.514$, $y_{S_I} = 0.375$; $6S_{II}$ in 6(h) : $x_{S_{II}} = 0.235$, $y_{S_{II}} = 0$.

A projection of the Th_7S_{12} structure onto the basal plane is shown in Fig. 28.

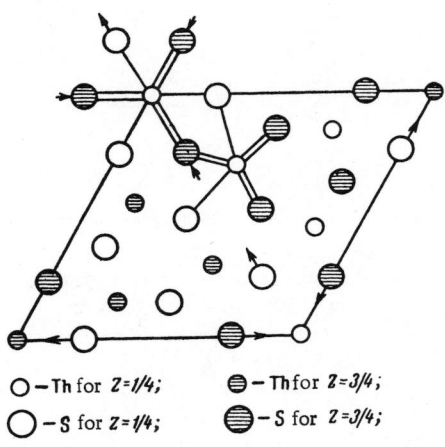

○ – Th for $Z = 1/4$;   ⊖ – Th for $Z = 3/4$;
○ – S for $Z = 1/4$;   ⊖ – S for $Z = 3/4$;

Fig. 28. Projection of the Th_7S_{12} structure onto the (0001) plane, after Zachariasen.

Since there is only one thorium atom, Th_I, for two 2(a) positions in Th_7S_{12}, the structure has some characteristics of disorder, so that the chemical composition of the compound $ThS_{1.71 \to 1.76}$ may vary. It is clear that the limiting compositions of this compound must be $Th_8S_{12} = Th_2S_3$, when the 2(a) positions are completely occupied by two Th_I atoms, and $Th_6S_{12} = ThS_2$, when the 2(a) positions are entirely vacant, i.e., the phase has the variable composition $ThS_{1.5 \to 2.0}$.

Because of this disorder there is some uncertainty in the atomic parameters of S_{II} along the x axis; namely, $x_{S_{II}}$ may vary in the range 0.215—0.255; the mean value is $x_{S_{II}}$ = 0.235. This leads to possible displacements of the S_{II} atoms, the limits of which are marked by arrows in Fig. 28.

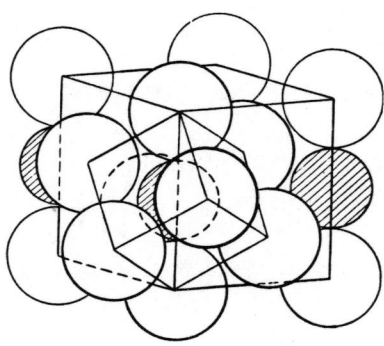

Fig. 29. Crystal structure of αUO_3 [82]. Uranium atoms are shown shaded; coordination around the uranium atom, involving oxygen atoms from neighboring cells is shown.

The coordination numbers and nearest interatomic distances (in Å) are:

$$Th_I - 3S_{II} = 2.82 \qquad Th_{II} - 2S_I = 2.95$$
$$- 6S_{II} = 3.09 \qquad - 3S_I = 2.98$$
$$- 2S_{II} = 2.85$$
$$- 1S_{II} = 3.00$$

The average values of the Th — S interatomic distances in Th_7S_{12} (in Å) fit satisfactorily into the general series of thorium sulfides [77]:

$$ThS : Th - 6S = 2.83;$$
$$Th_2S_3 : Th - 7S = 2.90; \qquad \text{(cont'd)}$$

Th_7S_{12} : Th — 9S = 3.00;
Th — 8S = 2.94;
ThS_2 : Th — 9S = 2.95.

The thorium atoms are not in mutual contact.

2. α UO_3 type [69]. The structure is hexagonal, with one formula unit in the unit cell. The lattice constants for UO_3: a= 3.971; c= 4.168 kX.

Space group D_{3d}^3 — $C\bar{3}m$; atomic coordinates: 1U in 1(a); 1O_I in 1(b); 2 O_{II} in 2(d), z = 0.17.

The structure of $\alpha\,UO_3$ is shown in Fig. 29.

Each uranium atom is surrounded by six O_I atoms at a distance of 2.08 A, and six O_{II} atoms at a distance of 2.39 A. Infinite "uranyl" chains — O_I — U — O_I — U — penetrate the crystal in the direction of the hexagonal axis.

HYDROGEN AND SUBGROUP VIIb

The compositions and crystal structure types of chemical compounds of hydrogen and the halogens with thorium, uranium, plutonium, and neptunium are given in Table 23.

The known structural types are represented by the following compounds:

ZrF_4 type: ThF_4 ($a=$ 13.1 kX; $b=$ 11.0 kX; $c=$ 8.6 kX; $\beta=$ 126°);

UF_4 ($a=$ 12.79 kX; $b=$ 10.72 kX; $c=$ 8.39 kX; $\beta=$ 126°10');

PuF_4 ($a=$ 12.59 kX; $b=$ 10.55 kX; $c=$ 8.26 kX; $\beta=$ 126°10');

NpF_4 ($a=$ 12.67 kX; $b=$ 10.62 kX; $c=$ 8.31 kX; $\beta=$ 126°10');

LaF_3 type: UF_3 ($a=$ 4.138 kX; $c=$ 7.333 kX);

PuF_3 ($a=$ 4.087 kX; $c=$ 7.240 kX);

NpF_3 ($a=$ 4.108 kX; $c=$ 7.273 kX);

CaF_2 type: $PuH_{2 \rightarrow 3}$ (where PuH_2: $a=$ 5.359 A).

$\beta W = W_3O$ type [82; 90]: α UH_3 ($a=$ 4.160 A).

Compounds of hydrogen and the halogens with the actinides form a great variety of new structural types, of which the following have been determined: $ThH_2(ThD_2)$; βUH_3 (UD_3); Th_4H_{15}; U_2F_9; αUF_5; βUF_5; UCl_3; UCl_4; UCl_6 and $PuBr_3$. These types are considered below.

1. ThH_2 (ThD_2) type [85]. The structure, determined by neutron diffraction for thorium dideuteride, belongs to the tetragonally distorted CaF_2 type with four formula units in the cell. The lattice constants for ThH_2 are $a=$ 4.10 A; $c=$ 5.03 A for a body-centered tetragonal cell. The thorium atoms are in the 000 and $\frac{1}{2}\frac{1}{2}\frac{1}{2}$ positions, and the hydrogen atoms in the $0\frac{11}{24}$, $\frac{1}{2}0\frac{1}{4}$, $\frac{1}{2}0\frac{3}{4}$, $0\frac{13}{24}$ positions.

TABLE 23

SUBGROUP VIIb AND HYDROGEN

	H			F			Cl			Br			I		
	Formula of compounds	Structure type	Lit. source	Formula of compounds	Structure type	Lit. source	Formula of compounds	Structure type	Lit. source	Formula of compounds	Structure type	Lit. source	Formula of compounds	Structure type	Lit. source
Th	$ThH_2(ThD_2)$	CaF_2	[85]	ThF_4	ZrF_4	[67]	$ThCl_4$	UCl_4	[70]	$ThBr_4$	UCl_4	[71]	ThI_2	CdI_2	[82]
	Th_4H_{15}	Th_4H_{15}	[86]												
	αUH_3	$\beta W = W_3O$	[87]	UF_3	LaF_3	[67]	UCl_3	UCl_3	[68]	UBr_3	UCl_3	[68]	UI_3	$PuBr_3$	[69]
	$\beta UH_3(\beta UD_3)$	$\beta UH_3(\beta UD_3)$	[88]	UF_4	ZrF_4	[67]	UCl_4	UCl_4	[70]	UBr_4		[1]			
				U_4F_{17}		[1]	UCl_5		[72]						
				U_2F_9	U_2F_9	[72]	UCl_6	UCl_6	[73]						
				αUF_5	αUF_5	[73]			[1]						
				βUF_5	βUF_5	[73]			[75]						
				UF_6		[1]									
Pu	$PuH_{2\div 3}$	CaF_2	[21,89]	PuF_3	LaF_3	[67]	$PuCl_3$	UCl_3	[68]	$PuBr_3$	$PuBr_3$	[69]	PuI_3	$PuBr_3$	[69]
				PuF_4	ZrF_4	[67]	$PuCl_4$		[67]						
Np				NpF_3	LaF_3	[67]	$NpCl_3$	UCl_3	[68]	$\alpha NpBr_3$	UCl_3	[68]	NpI_3	$PuBr_3$	[69]
				NpF_4	ZrF_4	[67]	$NpCl_4$	UCl_4	[67]	$\beta NpBr_3$	$PuBr_3$	[67]			
				NpF_6		[1]			[1]	$NpBr_4$		[1]			

The coordination numbers and nearest interatomic distances (in A) are:

$$D - 4Th = 2.41 \qquad Th - 8D = 2.41$$
$$- 8Th = 3.83$$
$$- 4Th = 4.09$$

The interatomic distances Th — Th = 3.83 A proved unexpectedly large in comparison with the corresponding distances in pure metallic thorium. This indicates the significant role of Th — D(H) bonds in the total balance of interatomic bonding in ThD_2. Thorium dihydride has metallic properties, and therefore the distances Th — D = 2.41 A are relatively large.

2. Th_4H_{15} type [86]. The highest hydride of thorium has a chemical composition which does not correspond to the simple stoichiometric formula ThH_4; as Zachariasen showed [86], its composition is Th_4H_{15}. The crystal structure is cubic, body-centered, with four formula units in the unit cell. The lattice constant of Th_4H_{15}: $a = 9.11$ A.

Space group $T_d^6 - J\bar{4}3d$; atomic coordinates: 16Th in 16(c), $x = 0.208$; $12H_I$ in 12(a); $48H_{II}$ in 48(e), $x = 0.400$, $y = 0.230$, $z = 0.372$.

The projection of the Th_4H_{15} structure onto the cube face of the unit cell is shown in Fig. 30.

The coordination numbers and nearest interatomic distances (in A) are:

$$\begin{array}{ll} Th - 3Th = 3.87 & H_I - 4Th = 2.46 \\ - 2Th = 3.95 & - 4H_{II} = 2.38 \\ - 3Th = 4.10 & H_{II} - 3Th = 2.29 \\ - 3H_I = 2.46 & - 2H_{II} = 2.02 \\ - 9H_{II} = 2.29 & \end{array}$$

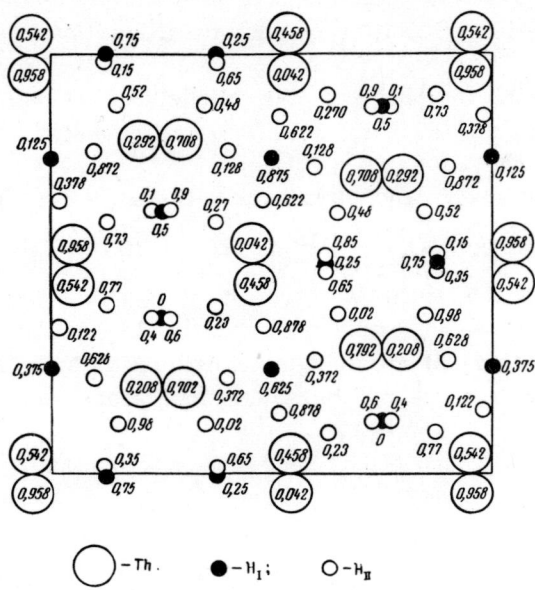

Fig. 30. Projection of the Th_4H_{15} structure onto the cube face of the unit cell. The numbers correspond to the third coordinate.

The thorium atoms are far from mutual contact. Each thorium atom is surrounded by 12 hydrogen atoms at distances from 2.29 to 2.46 A; subtraction of the atomic radius of metallic thorium (1.79 A) gives 0.67 and 0.50 A for the atomic radii of H_I and H_{II} respectively. The H_I atoms lie at centers of almost regular tetrahedrons of thorium atoms. The H_{II} atoms lie at centers of triangles formed by thorium atoms; these triangles are almost equilateral (3.87; 3.95 and 4.01 A).

It should be noted that the positions of thorium atoms in Th_4H_{15} exactly correspond to the positions of silicon atoms in $Cu_{15}Si_4$, the structure of which was established in 1934 by Morral and Westgren [82]. The compounds Th_4H_{15} and $Cu_{15}Si_4$ are isostructural both stoichiometrically and in the positions of the thorium and silicon atoms; this was not noticed by Zachariasen [86]. The positions of hydrogen atoms in Th_4H_{15} differ greatly from the positions of copper atoms in $Cu_{15}Si_4$, but it should be noted that

Zachariasen's values for the atomic coordinates of hydrogen in Th_4H_{15} require confirmation by neutron diffraction.

3. $\beta UH_3(UD_3)$ type [88]. The structure is cubic, with eight formula units in the unit cell. The lattice constant $a = 6.63$ kX.

The space group and atomic coordinates were determined by neutron diffraction: O_h^3 -- Pm3n; $2U_I$ in 2(a); $6U_{II}$ in 6(c); 24H(D) in 24(k), $y = 0.155$, $z = 0.31$.

The projection of the βUH_3 structure onto a cube face is shown in Fig. 31, where the numbers near the atoms represent heights

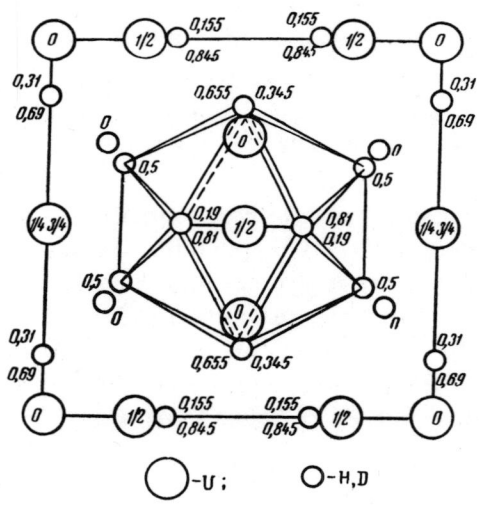

Fig. 31. Projection of the βUH_3 structure onto a cube face. Coordination around a central U_1 atom is shown; the numbers correspond to height along the third coordinate.

along the third coordinate, in fractions of cell edge. The bond lines represent coordination of 12 hydrogen (or deuterium) atoms, at the corners of a somewhat irregular icosahedron, around the U_I atom. Each U_{II} atom is also surrounded by 12 hydrogen atoms in groups of three at the corners of a truncated tetrahedron, each such group of three forming the face of a separate icosahedron around a U_I atom. Each hydrogen atom lies at the center of a deformed tetrahedron at the corners of which there are four uranium atoms, at the same distance within the limits of experimental accuracy. All the uranium—hydrogen interatomic distances are equal: $U_I - H = U_{II} - H = 2.32$ A.

Thus, if the usual concepts of atomic radii are applicable to metallic hydrides, the hydrogen atoms are present in enormous voids of the uranium portion of the lattice. If the atomic radius of uranium with coordination number 12 is taken as 1.52 A, the atomic radius of hydrogen becomes 0.80 A, which is three times the "normal" hydrogen radius.

The U -- U and H -- H distances are very large in comparison with the corresponding sums of the atomic radii. Therefore interatomic bonding in UH_3 is effected mainly by uranium—hydrogen interaction. Since the formation of uranium hydride is accompanied by very great expansion of uranium (increase of U -- U interatomic distances), the long U -- H bonds cannot be ascribed to the filling of existing voids in the lattice of metallic uranium. The hydrogen voids are caused by formation of uranium hydride. Similarly, the long U -- H bonds cannot be interpreted as the consequence of weak uranium—hydrogen interaction, as UH_3 is formed with considerable liberation of heat.

Some kind of additional information is required for correct interpretation of the experimentally found long metal—hydrogen bonds in the hydrides of heavy metals.

4. U_2F_9 type [72]. The structure is cubic, with four formula units in the unit cell. The lattice constant of U_2F_9: $a = 8.4545$ kX.

Space group T_d^3 — $J\bar{4}3m$; atomic coordinates: 8U in 8(c), $x = 0.187$; 12F_I in 12(e), $x = 0.225$; 24F_{II} in 24(g), $x = 0.20$, $z = 0.46$.

The projection of the U_2F_9 structure onto the cube face of the unit cell is shown in Fig. 32.

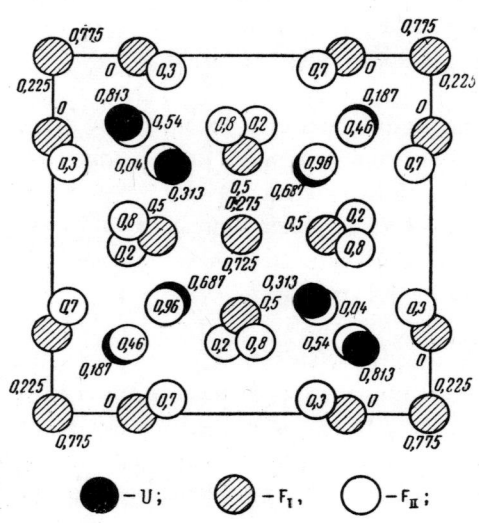

Fig. 32. Projection of the U_2F_9 structure onto the cube face of the unit cell. The numbers correspond to the third coordinate.

The coordination numbers and interatomic distances (in A) are:

$$\begin{array}{ll} U - 3F_I = 2.26 & F_I - F_I = 2.69 \\ - 3F_{II} = 2.31 & F_I - F_{II} = 2.57 \\ - 3F_{II} = 2.34 & F_{II} - F_{II} = 2.58 \end{array}$$

The uranium atoms are not in mutual contact. An interesting feature of the U_2F_9 structure is the structural equivalence of all the uranium atoms (ions), since they occupy a single regular system of 8(c) points. Each uranium atom is surrounded by nine fluorine atoms at the average distance U — 9F = 2.31 A. Thus, representation of the chemical structure of U_2F_9 by the formulas $UF_4 \cdot UF_5$ or $UF_6 \cdot 3UF_4$ is unjustified from the crystallographic aspect. Each uranium atom in U_2F_9 has the same electronic structure, corresponding to the fractional valence 4 1/2.

5. α UF_5 type [73]. The structure is tetragonal, with two formula units in the unit cell. The lattice constants of αUF_5: a = 6.512 kX; c = 4.463 kX.

Space group C_{4h}^5 — $J4/m$; atomic coordinates: 2U in 2(a); $2F_I$ in 2(b); $8F_{II}$ in 8(h), x = 0.315, y = 0.113.

The crystal structure of αUF_5 is shown in Fig. 33.

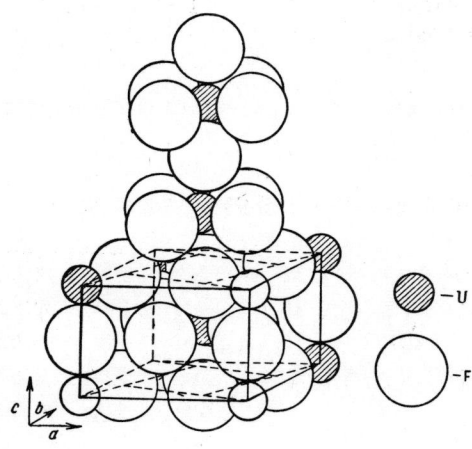

Fig. 33. Crystal structure of αUF_5. Chains of $UF_4(F^{1/2})_2$ octahedrons parallel to the tetragonal axis are shown.

The nearest interatomic distances (in A) are:

$$U - 2F_I = 2.23 \qquad F_I - F_{II} = 2.78$$
$$ - 4F_{II} = 2.18 \qquad F_{II} - F_{II} = 2.82$$

All the uranium atoms are structurally equivalent. Each uranium atom lies at the center of an octahedron of fluorine atoms, slightly extended axially. The octahedrons are joined at their vertices through F_I atoms, forming chains in the direction of the Z axis. The bonding between uranium and fluorine atoms is predominantly ionic. The ionic radius of $U^{5+} = 0.87$ A.

6. β UF_5 type [73]. The structure is tetragonal, with eight formula units in the unit cell. The lattice constants for βUF_5: $a = 11.450$ kX; $c = 5.198$ kX.

Space group D_{2d}^{12} -- J42D; atomic coordinates: 8U in 8(d), $x = 0.083$; $8F_I$ in 8(d), $x = 0.273$, $16F_{II}$ in 16(e), $x = 0.15$, $y = 0.07$, $z = 0.05$; $16F_{III}$ in 16(e); $x = 0.05$, $y = 0.14$, $z = 0.46$.

The projection of the β UF_5 structure onto the (001) plane is shown in Fig. 34.

The nearest interatomic distances (in A) are:

$$U - 1F_I = 2.18 \qquad F_I - F_I = 2.66$$
$$ - 2F_{II} = 2.23 \qquad F_I - F_{II} = 2.52$$
$$ - 2F_{II} = 2.29 \qquad F_{II} - F_{II} = 2.92$$
$$ - 2F_{III} = 2.18 \qquad F_I - F_{III} = 2.54$$
$$\phantom{U - 2F_{III} = 2.18 \qquad} F_{III} - F_{III} = 2.44$$
$$\phantom{U - 2F_{III} = 2.18 \qquad} F_{II} - F_{III} = 2.55$$

All the uranium atoms are structurally equivalent. Each uranium atom is surrounded by seven fluorine atoms. The short interionic F -- F distances suggest that covalent bonding between the fluorine atoms is not excluded.

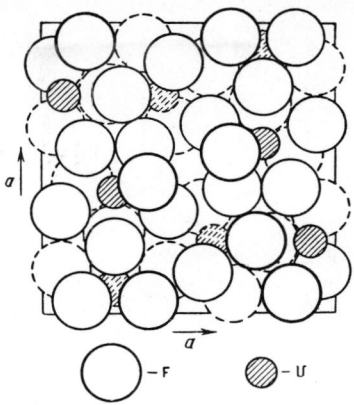

Fig. 34. Projection of the β UF$_5$ structure onto the (001) plane [82].

7. UCl$_3$ type [68]. The structure is hexagonal, with two formula units in the unit cell. The lattice constants (in A) for isostructural compounds are: for UCl$_3$: a = 7.428, c = 4.312; NpCl$_3$: a = 7.405, c = 4.273; PuCl$_3$: a = 7.380, c = 4.238; UBr$_3$: a = 7.926, c = 4.432; αNpBr$_3$: a = 7.917, c = 4.382.

Space group C_{6h}^2 — C6$_3$/m; atomic coordinates: 2U in 2(a); 6Cl in 6(h), x = 0.375, y = 0.292.

The projection of the UCl$_3$ structure onto the (0001) plane, for four unit cells, is shown in Fig. 35.

The nearest interatomic distances for UCl$_3$ are:

$$U - 3Cl = 2.95 \text{ A} \qquad Cl - Cl = 3.45 \text{ A}$$
$$- 6Cl = 2.96$$

The UCl$_3$ structural type belongs to the coordination class. The interatomic bonds are predominantly ionic in character. Each uranium atom is surrounded by nine chlorine atoms at almost equal distances. The Cl -- Cl = 0.45 A bond is somewhat shorter than the sum of two ionic radii for chlorine (3.62 A).

111

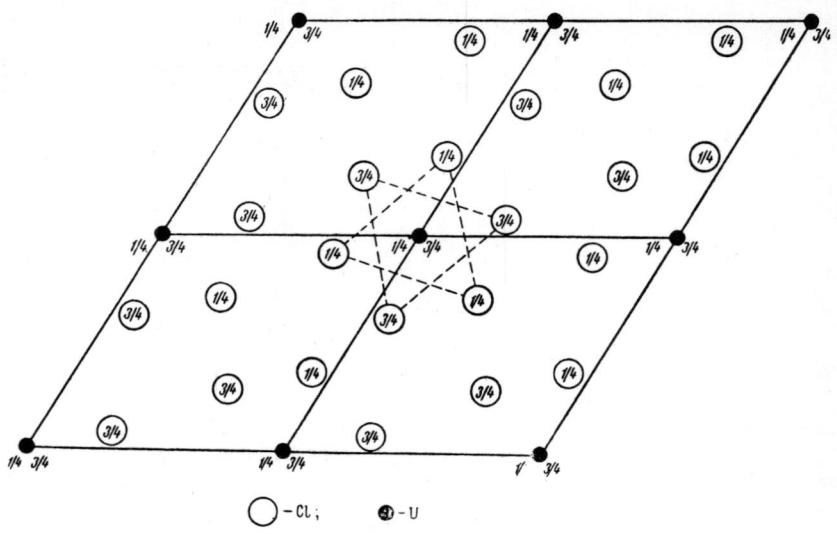

Fig. 35. Projection of the UCl$_3$ structure onto the (0001) plane for four unit cells. The coordination of nine Cl atoms around a U atom is shown; the numbers represent the third coordinate.

8. **UCl$_4$ type [70].** The structure is tetragonal, with four formula units in the unit cell. The lattice constants (in A) for isostructural compounds are: for ThCl$_4$: $a = 8.473$, $c = 7.468$; UCl$_4$: $a = 8.296$, $c = 7.487$; ThBr$_4$: $a = 8.945$, $c = 7.930$.

Space group D_{4h}^{19} — $J4/amd$; atomic coordinates: 4U in 4(a); 16Cl in 16(h), $x = 0.280$, $z = 0.916$.

The crystal structure of UCl$_4$ (ThCl$_4$) is shown in Fig. 36.

The shortest interatomic distances (in A) are:

$$U - 4Cl = 2.41 \qquad 1 - Cl = 3.2$$
$$- 4Cl = 3.09$$

Each uranium atom is surrounded, in very flattened tetrahedral coordination, by four nearest chlorine atoms at distance U — 4Cl =

= 2.41 A. The short Cl — Cl = 3.2 A bonds indicate interaction in the chlorine portion of the lattice.

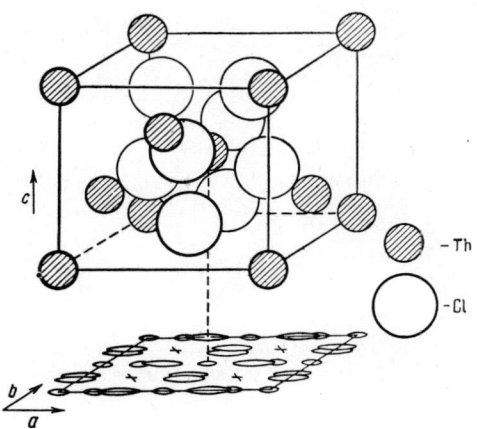

Fig. 36. Crystal structure of UCl$_4$ and ThCl$_4$ [82]. The projection of the structure onto the (001) plane is also shown.

9. UCl$_6$ type [75]. The structure is hexagonal, with three molecular UCl$_6$ units in the unit cell. The lattice constants for UCl$_6$: $a = 10.95$ kX; $c = 6.03$ kX.

Space group D_{3h}^3 — $C3\overline{m}$; atomic coordinates: 1U$_I$ in 1(a); 2U$_{II}$ in 2(d), $z = 0.5$; 6Cl$_I$ in 6(i), $x = 0.10$, $z = 0.25$; 6Cl$_{II}$ in 6(i), $x = 0.43$, $z = 0.25$; 6Cl$_{III}$ in 6(i), $x = 0.77$, $z = 0.25$.

The projection of the UCl$_6$ structure onto the basal plane of the unit cell is shown in Fig. 37; it is seen that UCl$_6$ has a typical molecular structure with distinctly formed UCl$_6$ molecules. Each uranium atom is surrounded by six chlorine atoms in an almost exact octahedron, with distances U — Cl = 2.42 A. The nearest distance between chlorine atoms in neighboring UCl$_6$ molecules is 3.85 A.

The molecular character of the UCl₆ structure is consistent with the high volatility of this compound.

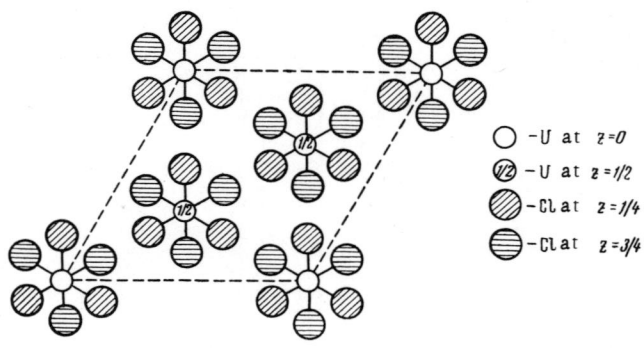

Fig. 37. Projection of the UCl$_6$ structure onto the (0001) plane, after Zachariasen.

10. PuBr$_3$ type [69]. The structure is rhombic, with four formula units in the unit cell. The lattice constants (in kX) for isostructural compounds are: for PuBr$_3$: a = 12.62, b = 4.09, c = 9.13; β NpBr$_3$: a = 12.65, b = 4.11, c = 9.15; UI$_3$: a = 13.98, b = 4.31, c = 9.99; NpI$_3$: a = 14.00, b = 4.29, c = 9.93; PuI$_3$: a = 14.00, b = 4.29, c = 9.90.

Space group D_{2h}^{17} — Cmcm; atomic coordinates: 4Pu in 4(c), x = 0.25; 4Br$_I$ in 4(c), x = −0.07; 8Br$_{II}$ in 8(f), x = 0.36, z = 0.05.

Part of the PuBr$_3$ structure is shown in Fig. 38.

Infinite networks of plutonium atoms and networks of bromine atoms, in alternate superposition, extend at right angles to the a axis. Each plutonium atom is surrounded by eight bromine atoms at a distance of 3.08 Å. Zachariasen [69] did not give a detailed description of the PuBr$_3$ type of structure.

We have now considered the crystal structure of numerous chemical compounds of uranium, thorium, plutonium, and neptunium with elements of the b subgroups, in the series of rising subgroup numbers.

As we pass from metals of subgroup Ib to halogens of subgroup VIIb, the metallic properties of the elements become gradually weaker, with transition to typical nonmetals. As is known from

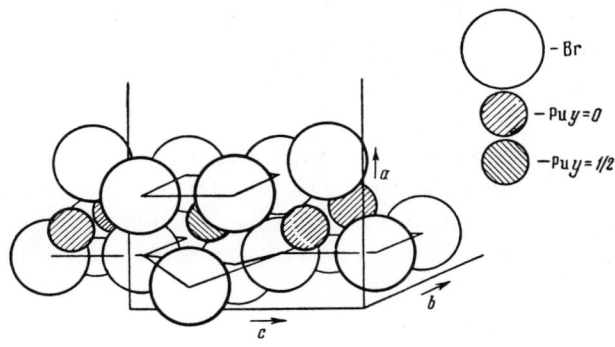

Fig. 38. Part of the PuBr$_3$ structure [82].

general crystal chemistry, for many elements of the b subgroups this is manifested in the formation of the so-called "8--N" structures (where N is the number of the subgroup). In these structures each atom has 8--N nearest neighbors, with the formation of 8--N covalent bonds, which stand out on a general background of metallic or van der Waals bonding. This type of structure is found in hexagonal networks of zinc and cadmium atoms, in the rhombohedral network of mercury atoms, in diatomic gallium "molecules," in the tetrahedral frameworks of germanium and α-tin atoms, in puckered layers of arsenic, antimony, or bismuth atoms, in screw chains of selenium or tellurium atoms, and in diatomic halogen molecules--all in crystals of the corresponding elements.

Thus, even the original crystal structures of the elements in the b subgroups are themselves crudely heterodesmic, i.e., heterogeneous in the nature of their interatomic bonding.

In compounds of the elements of the b subgroups with the actinide elements the heterodesmic nature of the crystal structures is even more pronounced because of superposition of heteropolar interaction between the atoms and formation of ionic bonds. The effects of ionic and covalent bonding ultimately lead to the formation of "normal-valence" compounds of constant composition; this is especially pronounced in compounds of nonmetals and of metals of the IVb, Vb, VIb, and VIIb subgroups with the actinides. Thus, halogens sometimes form purely molecular crystals with the actinides; for example, UCl_6, in which the crystals contain completely discrete UCl_6 molecules.

However, this example is somewhat of an exception, as in most cases the structures formed are not purely molecular, but of the coordination type, containing islands, chains, layers, or frameworks of like or unlike atoms, in which the interatomic bonding is predominantly covalent and the interatomic distances are accordingly shortened.

The valences of the atoms in these "condensed atomic groupings" (CAG) in crystals, and the quantitative characteristics of valence bonding between different CAG in a crystal are not generally known as yet, and their determination is an important scientific task for modern theoretical chemistry. Therefore the stoichiometry of most of the compounds considered here remains incomprehensible in the light of formal valence concepts. Even in certain halides, such as U_2F_9 discussed above, the formal valence of uranium, $4\frac{1}{2}$, is "abnormal" and incomprehensible. Such compounds as U_4F_1 or Th_4H_{15} are also inexplicable in terms of "normal" valences.

Examples of "condensed atomic groupings" in some of the known structural types of actinide compounds with elements of the b subgroups which were considered earlier are given below.

The structural type $CuAl_2$, represented by the compounds Th_2Cu, $Th_{2\pm x}Zn$, Th_2Al, is found only in compounds with metals of the Ib, IIb, and IIIb subgroups. It is characteristic for well-defined intermetallides, although it is heterodesmic.

Condensed covalent atomic groupings are:

a) infinite linear chains of copper, zinc, or aluminum atoms, running through the crystals in the direction of the Z axis;

b) diatomic Th_2 groups.

The structural type AlB_2 is represented by the compounds: $ThZn_2$, $ThAl_2$, βUSi_2 etc.

Condensed atomic groupings are:

a) hexagonal plane networks (parallel to the basal plane) with coordination number 3, composed of zinc, aluminum, or silicon atoms; the interatomic distances in the networks are greatly shortened.

The structural type $NaZn_{13}$ is represented by the compounds: $ThBe_{13}$, UBe_{13}, $NpBe_{13}$, $PuBe_{13}$. In this case the condensed atomic groupings are square tetrads of beryllium atoms with shortened interatomic distances.

The structural type $MgCu_2$ is represented by the compounds: UAl_2, $PuAl_2$, $NpAl_2$. The condensed atomic groupings are of a framework character:

a) aluminum atoms form a continuous tetrahedral framework with shortened interatomic distances within this framework;

b) uranium, plutonium, or neptunium atoms themselves form continuous tetrahedral frameworks (of the diamond type) with shortened interatomic distances;

c) CAG (a) is inserted into CAG (b), the interatomic (a)−(b) distances being greater than the sums of the corresponding atomic radii, rather than shorter.

Many examples of condensed atomic groupings can be found on examination of other known and new structural types described above.

V. ATOMIC RADII OF ACTINIDES IN CRYSTALS

A system of atomic radii corresponding to ionic, covalent, and metallic bonds for actinide elements in crystalline compounds was worked out by W. Zachariasen [1] on the basis of extensive experimental crystal-structure data on interatomic distances. Most of these data are considered in detail in Chapters II and III of this book.

A. F. Kapustinskii [104] theoretically calculated the ionic, covalent, and metallic radii of the atoms of transuranic elements from americium to mendelevium.

W. Zachariasen is quite justified in describing atomic radii in the crystalline state as "crystal radii."

Of course, at the present time there is some uncertainty in classifying particular crystalline compounds by the type of interatomic bonding: ionic, covalent (homopolar), metallic, or van der Waals bonding. This uncertainty is due to the lack of direct experimental methods for determination of the effective numbers of valence electrons involved in formation of interatomic bonds in various crystalline compounds. However, chemical composition and a number of chemical and physical properties of the compounds can be used to compare experimentally determined interatomic distances and to select certain groups of compounds which fit most closely into a particular type of chemical bonding. For example, halides and in particular fluorides form predominantly ionic M — F bonds, where M is an actinide element; sulfides and certain oxygen compounds form mainly covalent bonds (such as

U — O in the uranyl group); close-packed metals and intermetallides form metallic bonds.

Accordingly, *ionic, covalent,* and *metallic* radii are distinguished; the latter are often called simply atomic radii.

IONIC RADII OF THE ACTINIDES

Zachariasen [1] showed that the previously accepted values of atomic radii given in papers by V. M. Goldschmidt (1926) and L. Pauling (1927) are not satisfactory, as the interionic distances calculated from these radii differ by approximately 0.15 A from observed values. In 1954 Zachariasen revised the ionic radii for most elements (including the actinides) in the light of modern data.

The revision was based on experimentally determined interatomic distances in the corresponding fluorides, the value of 1.33 A for the fluorine anion being taken as standard.

Table 24 contains (after Zachariasen [1]) values for the ionic radii of elements the valence states of which correspond to ions with the electronic configuration of the corresponding inert gases.

TABLE 24

IONIC RADII OF VARIOUS ELEMENTS (A)

−2		O 1.46	S 1.90	Se 2.02	Te 2.22	Po 2.30
−1		F 1.33	Cl 1.81	Br 1.96	I 2.19	At 2.27
+1	Li 0.68	Na 0.98	K 1.33	Rb 1.48	Cs 1.67	Fr 1.75
+2	Be 0.30	Mg 0.65	Ca 0.94	Sr 1.10	Ba 1.29	Ra 1.37
+3	B 0.16	Al 0.45	Sc 0.68	Y 0.88	La 1.04	Ac 1.11
+4		Si 0.38	Ti 0.60	Zr 0.77	Ce 0.92	Th 0.99
+5				Nb 0.67		Pa 0.90
+6						U 0.83

(Valence column on the left)

Tables 25 and 26 contain (after Zachariasen [1]) the corresponding ionic radii of the lanthanide and actinide elements in different valence states.

TABLE 25

IONIC RADII OF THE LANTHANIDES AND THEIR NEIGHBORING ELEMENTS

Element	Ionic radius, A valence state			
	1+	2+	3+	4+
Cesium	1.67			
Barium		1.29		
Lanthanum			1.04	
Cerium			1.02	0.92
Praseodymium			1.00	0.90
Neodymium			0.99	
Promethium			(0.98)	
Samarium		1.11	0.97	
Europium		1.09	0.96	
Gadolinium			0.94	
Terbium			0.92	0.84
Dysprosium			0.91	
Erbium			0.89	
Holmium			0.87	
Thulium			0.86	
Ytterbium		0.93	0.85	
Lutetium			0.84	
Hafnium				0.77

The ionic radii of elements No. 96 to 102 have not been determined experimentally as yet.

COVALENT RADII OF THE ACTINIDES

The covalent radii of elements other than actinides have been given mainly by L. Pauling [91], and are to be found in text books of crystal chemistry [59]. Zachariasen [1] pointed out that at the present time there are very few experimental results for deter-

TABLE 26

IONIC RADII OF THE ACTINIDES

Atomic number	Element	Ionic radius			
		valence state			
		3+	4+	5+	6+
89	Actinium	1.11			
90	Thorium	(1.08)	0.99		
91	Protactinium	(1.05)	0.96	0.90	
92	Uranium	1.03	0.93	0.87	0.83
93	Neptunium	1.01	0.92	0.88	0.82
94	Plutonium	1.00	0.90	0.87	0.81
95	Americium	0.99	0.89	0.86	0.80

mination of reliable values of the covalent radii of the actinide elements. Therefore the single-bond covalent radii of the actinides, given in Table 27 after Zachariasen [1] may eventually need revision.

TABLE 27

COVALENT SINGLE-BOND RADII OF THE ACTINIDES

Element	Radius, A		
	valence state		
	4+	5+	6+
Thorium................	1.67		
Protactinium............	1.64	1.52	
Uranium................	1.62	1.50	1.42
Neptunium.............	1.60	1.49	1.41
Plutonium..............	1.58	1.48	1.40
Americium.............	1.57	1.47	1.39

METALLIC RADII OF THE ACTINIDES

Atomic radii corresponding to metallic bonding in crystals of elements are given for coordination number 12. If in real crystal structures the coordination number is less than 12, a correction is applied [6].

The metallic radii of the elements from francium to americium, after Zachariasen, are given in Table 28.

TABLE 28

METALLIC RADII OF ELEMENTS FRANCIUM TO AMERICIUM

Element	Metallic radius, Å					
	valence state					
	1+	2+	3+	4+	5+	6+
Francium	2.80					
Radium		2.35				
Actinium			2.03			
Thorium				(1.79)		
Protactinium				1.76	(1.63)	
Uranium			1.92	1.74	1.61	(1.54)
Neptunium			1.89	1.72	1.60	(1.52)
Plutonium			1.86	1.70	(1.60)	1.51
Americium			1.84	1.69	1.58	1.50

Experimental values are given in the table in parentheses; the remaining values were found by extrapolation or interpolation for various valence states.

VI. DUALITY OF THE CHEMICAL NATURE OF THORIUM, URANIUM, NEPTUNIUM, AND PLUTONIUM

PRELIMINARY CONCEPTS

Before the transuranium elements (neptunium, etc.) had been discovered and studied, the position of thorium, protactinium, and uranium in Mendeleev's periodic system gave rise to no doubts, and was as shown below:

Incomplete electron levels	Subgroups of elements			
	IVa	Va	VIa	VIIa
3d	Ti	V	Cr	Mn
4d	Zr	Nb	Mo	Tc
5d	Hf	Ta	W	Re
6d	Th	Pa	U	

The highest oxides: ThO_2, Pa_2O_5, and UO_3, were quite consistent with the position of thorium in subgroup IVa, of protactinium in subgroup Va, and of uranium in subgroup VIa. Thus thorium was formally regarded as the chemical analog of hafnium, zirconium, and titanium; protactinium, the analog of tantalum, niobium, and vanadium; and uranium, the analog of tungsten, molybdenum, and chromium. It was accordingly assumed that whereas in hafnium, tantalum, and tungsten atoms the 5d electron level undergoes completion, in the case of thorium, protactinium, and uranium atoms it is the 6d electron level. Therefore, in accordance with this theory, thorium, protactinium, and uranium might be described as "6d elements."

On the other hand, ever since the rare-earth family of elements had been discovered and studied the analogy of quadrivalent cerium and praseodymium to thorium has been well known. The chemical peculiarity of the rare-earth elements was explained theoretically by N. Bohr [92] in relation to the electronic structure of the atom, namely, filling of the 4f electron level. Subsequently this theory was confirmed by a mass of spectroscopic, magnetic, chemical, crystal-chemical, and other experimental evidence. Accordingly, V. M. Goldschmidt [93] gave the name of "lanthanides" to the elements from lanthanum to lutetium. Therefore the brief "electronic" term for the lanthanides should be "4f elements."

In working out the electron structure of atoms of the chemical elements in relation to the Bohr—Thomson periodic system, N. Bohr [94] predicted as long ago as 1923 the possible filling of the 5f level in elements at the end of the periodic system. In fact, it was soon found that there was some crystal-chemical evidence in favor of this idea. For example, V. M. Goldschmidt [95] drew attention to the isomorphism of the ThO_2 and UO_2 structures, with a smaller atomic radius of the metal in the case of UO_2, which could be attributed to "5f contraction" on entry of electrons into the 5f level, analogously to the "lanthanide contraction," otherwise known as the "4f contraction," discovered earlier, also by V. M. Goldschmidt [93].

However, the starting point of this series of "5f elements," i.e., the first element to have an electron in the 5f shell, could not be accurately predicted from Bohr's theory because of shielding effects and of the weak binding of electrons in the 5f shell [96]. V. M. Goldschmidt [95b] suggested that the first 5f electron appears in protactinium, and therefore thorium is the parent of the 5f series; he accordingly proposed the term "thorides" for the "5f elements," by analogy with "lanthanides" for the "4f elements." At the same time V. M. Goldschmidt held that the first 5f electron need not necessarily appear in protactinium, but that it may also appear in other neighboring elements of thorium, or even among the transuranium elements. Goldschmidt reserved the terms "actinides," "protactinides," and "uranides" for these cases. As is known, the term "actinides" has now been widely adopted.

THE 5f ELEMENTS

1. The "Actinide" Hypothesis

As soon as McMillan and Abelson discovered and studied the first transuranium element No. 93, neptunium [97] in 1940, the suspected existence of a family of "5f elements" analogous to the lanthanides was confirmed. If thorium, protactinium, uranium, and all the transuranium elements were "6d elements" by their electronic structure, the element following uranium--neptunium--should be the chemical analog of rhenium. In reality, neptunium greatly resembled uranium in its chemical properties, and was quite unlike rhenium. McMillan and Abelson considered that the parent of this new family of "5f elements" is uranium, and proposed the term "uranides" for all the elements following it.

In 1942, in studying plutonium and neptunium, Seaborg and Wahl [98] suggested that either actinium or thorium is the parent or zero element of the 5f series. The course of development of subsequent ideas in this field is very well outlined in a review article by Seaborg [99], who also gives numerous references to original literature sources.

Detailed consideration of the chemical, spectroscopic, magnetic, and crystallographic properties of the elements from actinium to californium led Seaborg [99] to the conclusion that the most likely parent of the family of "5f elements" is actinium, and therefore it should be termed the "actinide series," although this does not mean that the first 5f electron must necessarily appear in thorium.

The coalescence and spreading of the 5f and 6d electron levels are characteristic of the consecutive series of atoms of the transactinium elements, as shown schematically in Fig. 39, after Seaborg [99].

The curves for the binding energy of electrons in the 5f and 6d levels as a function of the atomic number (Fig. 39) are, of course, only rough and qualitative, but their validity in principle is justified

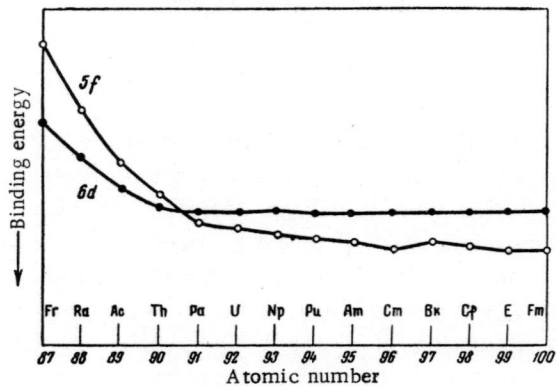

Fig. 39. Qualitative representation of the binding energy of 5 f and 6d electrons in the heavy elements, after Seaborg.

by all modern experimental and theoretical results. The energy of electron transfer between the 5f and 6d levels is found to be comparable with chemical bonding energy; this may result in the simultaneous participation of 5f and 6d electrons in the formation of chemical bonds in the corresponding compounds. The electronic structure of atoms of the transactinium elements may vary from compound to compound, and depends to a great extent on temperature and other factors which determine the physical state of the compounds. As already pointed out in Chapter III, this is vividly illustrated by the remarkable number and diversity of polymorphic forms of uranium, neptunium, and plutonium.

Thus, as Seaborg [99] also points out, the transactinium elements might be more properly characterized as elements of the "5f—6d range" rather than strictly as "5f elements" in the light of their electron structure.

Because of the existence of this "5f—6d range," the actinides have a considerably greater diversity of stable valence states than the lanthanides, where the 4f and 5d levels are more highly

TABLE 29

ELECTRON CONFIGURATIONS OF "GASEOUS" ATOMS OF ACTINIDES AND LANTHANIDES (BEYOND THE STRUCTURES OF XENON AND RADON)

Atomic number	Element	Electron configuration
57	Lanthanum	$5d6s^2$
58	Cerium	$4f^2 6s^2$
59	Praseodymium	$4f^3 6s^2$
60	Neodymium	$4f^4 6s^2$
61	Promethium	$4f^5 6s^2$
62	Samarium	$4f^6 6s^2$
63	Europium	$4f^7 6s^2$
64	Gadolinium	$4f^7 5d6s^2$
65	Terbium	$4f^9 6s^2$
66	Dysprosium	$4f^{10} 6s^2$
89	Actinium	$6d7s^2$
90	Thorium	$6d^2 7s^2$ or $5f6d7s^2$
91	Protactinium	$5f^2 6d7s^2$ or $5f6d^2 7s^2$
92	Uranium	$5f^3 6d7s^2$
93	Neptunium	$5f^5 7s^2$ or $5f^4 6d7s^2$
94	Plutonium	$5f^6 7s^2$ or $5f^5 6d7s^2$
95	Americium	$5f^7 7s^2$
96	Curium	$5f^7 6d7s^2$
97	Berkelium	$5f^9 7s^2$
98	Californium	$5f^{10} 7s^2$

differentiated. Usually any lanthanide element cannot have more than two valence states: +3 and +4, or +3 and +2. In the actinides, on the other hand, as analysis of the stoichiometric ratios of the oxides, sulfides and halides (see Tables 21, 22, and 23) shows, every element after thorium has four bona fide valence states: +3, +4, +5, and +6, and also the +2 subvalent state in monoxides and "inexplicable" fractional valences in such compounds as the fluorides U_2F_9 and U_4F_{17}.

Suggested electron configurations (beyond the radon and xenon structures) for "gaseous" atoms of actinides and lanthanides are given in Table 29, after Seaborg [99].

Mention must be made of Seaborg's comment [99] that "although many interesting and perspicacious proposals had been made up to this time, the electronic structure and place in the periodic table of these (5f--E. M.) elements could not be regarded as established."

2. The "Thoride" Hypothesis

W. Zachariasen [1] considers that the parent or zero element of the 5f series is not actinium, but thorium, as V. M. Goldschmidt had suggested earlier [95b]. Accordingly, the "5f elements" should be called "thorides."

Indeed, the stable trivalent state is unknown for thorium and protactinium, and there are no grounds for believing that the first 5f electron in thorium is consistent with the "actinide" hypothesis. The quadrivalent state is stable for thorium. The chemical properties of both thorium and protactinium are very unlike those of trivalent actinium, and therefore Zachariasen considers that these two elements can in no way be regarded as actinides.

On the other hand, if the group of "5f elements" as a whole is compared with the group of "4f elements," a general increase of valence is seen in the former; this is illustrated in Table 30 which gives the valences of the 4f and 5f elements (after Zachariasen).

TABLE 30

VALENCE STATES OF THE 5f AND 4f ELEMENTS

5f elements	Valence	4f elements	Valence
Actinium	3	Lanthanum	3
Thorium	4	Cerium	3,4
Protactinium	4,5	Praseodymium	3,4
Uranium	6,4,3,5	Neodymium	3
Neptunium	4,3,6,5	Promethium	
Plutonium	4,3,6,5	Samarium	3,2
Americium	3,4,6,5	Europium	2,3

Thus, the "average" valence of the 5f elements oscillates about the value of 4 in the 5f elements, in full agreement with the "thoride" hypothesis of Goldschmidt and Zachariasen, whereas the "average" and characteristic valence of the lanthanides is 3.

3. The "5f Contraction"

It has already been mentioned that V. M. Goldschmidt [95] was the first to suggest the possible existence of 5f contraction, analogous to the 4f contraction in lanthanides, on the basis of the isomorphism of ThO_2 and UO_2 and of the smaller atomic radius of U in comparison with Th. The existence of 5f contraction was conclusively proved by the extensive crystal-chemical investigations of Zachariasen. The series of dioxides, initiated by Goldschmidt, was continued by Zachariasen, and it now has the following form:

TABLE 31

DIMENSIONS OF THE MeO$_2$ UNIT CELL, CUBIC STRUCTURE OF THE FLUORITE TYPE (IN Å)

MeO$_2$	a	MeO$_2$	a
ThO$_2$	5.597 ± 0.001	NpO$_2$	5.436 ± 0.001
PaO$_2$	5.507 ± 0.002	PuO$_2$	5.397 ± 0.001
UO$_2$	5.468 ± 0.001	AmO$_2$	5.388 ± 0.003

This effect, in which there is a monotonic decrease of interatomic distances in isostructural compounds of the 5f elements with increase of the atomic number, has been named the "5f contraction." Formally it is quite analogous to the 4f contraction in the lanthanides, and is attributed to consecutive entry of electrons into the 5f shells of the atoms with increase of atomic number.

Other series of isostructural compounds of 5f elements, illustrating 5f contraction, are revealed by analysis of the crystal-chemical data in Chapter IV. The 5f contraction is illustrated especially vividly by the decrease in the ionic, covalent, and metallic radii of the 5f elements in identical valence states, as shown in Tables 26, 27, and 28.

The lanthanide contraction of the 4f elements is illustrated by the ionic radii given in Table 25.

As Zachariasen [1] points out, "the extremely close similarity in structure and interatomic distances in compounds of the 5f elements cannot be explained unless the configuration of the bonding electrons is identical, and additional electrons must accordingly be nonbonding 5f electrons." The isostructural character of chemically related compounds is due to the isoelectronic configuration of the interatomic bonds.

Thus, the formation of series of isostructural compounds and the existence of the 5f contraction effect are crystal-chemical proofs of the existence of 5f electrons in the "actinide" or "thoride" elements.

SIMILARITY OF THE 5f ELEMENTS TO THE ELEMENTS OF SUBGROUPS IVa, Va, AND VIa

At the present time it is most usual to regard thorium, protactinium, uranium, and the transuranium elements as "5f elements." As shown earlier, in Seaborg's more concrete interpretation actinium is considered to be the zero element of the 5f series, and all the 5f elements are therefore termed "actinides." The term "actinides" has become so widely adopted that it has to be used despite its doubtful validity. The term "thorides," proposed by Zachariasen, is less usual.

This success of the "5f theory," created by such important authorities as Seaborg, Zachariasen, and others (despite certain differences in detail), has obscured the undoubted similarity of the actinides to the "d elements" of the transition subgroups IVa (titanium, zirconium, hafnium), Va (vanadium, niobium, tantalum), and VIa (chromium, molybdenum, tungsten), and because of this and the extensive use of the term "actinides" the long-established similarity of thorium, protactinium, and uranium to the elements of subgroups IVa, Va, and VIa (which we shall call the IVa, Va, and VIa elements for the sake of brevity) has been almost entirely forgotten and disregarded. Nevertheless, there are no grounds for forgetting this similarity.

Despite the fact that the presence of 5f electrons in the transactinium elements has now been proved, we must not ignore the resemblance of these elements to the IVa, Va, and VIa elements, and regard the transactinium elements merely as 5f elements. This would be contrary to a wealth of experimental data confirming the existence of crystal-chemical analogies between compounds of the actinides on the one hand, and compounds of the IVa, Va, and VIa elements on the other.

In reality, we shall see that the resemblance between these groups of elements is so far-reaching that there is every reason to regard the transactinium elements not merely as 5f elements, but simultaneously as 6d elements. This duality in the chemical nature of the transactinium elements has a satisfactory qualitative explanation in the similarity of the energy states of their 5f and 6d electrons, as shown in Fig. 39 (see p. 126).

We now consider the crystal-chemical analogies in the compounds of actinide, lanthanide, and IVa, Va, and VIa elements.

Table 32 is a summary of different groups of isostructural compounds formed by the actinide, lanthanide, and IVa, Va, and VIa elements; from halides and hydrides, through oxides, sulfides, nitrides, carbides, silicides, and borides, to intermetallides. This

TABLE 32

ISOSTRUCTURAL COMPOUNDS OF ACTINIDE, LANTHANIDE, AND IVa, Va, AND VIa ELEMENTS

Compound type	Structure type	Actinide compounds	IVa, Va, VIa compounds	Lanthanide compounds
Halides	ZrF_4	ThF_4; UF_4; NpF_4; PuF_4	ZrF_4; HfF_4	CeF_4
Halides	LaF_3	AcF_3; UF_3; NpF_3; PuF_3; AmF_3		LaF_3; CeF_3; PrF_3; NdF_3; SmF_3
Halides	UCl_3	UCl_3; $AcCl_3$; $NpCl_3$; $PuCl_3$; $AmCl_3$; UBr_3; $AcBr_3$; $NpBr_3$		$LaCl_3$; $CeCl_3$; $PrCl_3$; $NdCl_3$; $LaBr_3$; $CeBr_3$; $PrBr_3$
Hydrides	ThD_2	ThH_2; ThD_2	ZrH_2; ZrD_2	
Oxides, sulfides, selenides and tellurides	NaCl	UO; PaO; NpO; PuO; AmO; ThS; US; PuS; ThSe; USe; UTe; PuTe	$TiO_{0.6 \rightarrow 1.25}$; VO; NbO	CeS; EuS; EuSe; EuTe; YbSe; YbTe
Oxides, sulfides, selenides and tellurides	La_2O_3	Pu_2O_3; Ac_2O_3		La_2O_3; Ce_2O_3; Pr_2O_3; Nd_2O_3
Oxides, sulfides, selenides and tellurides	CaF_2	PaO_2; NpO_2; PuO_2; AmO_2; ThO_2; UO_2	ZrO_2; HfO_2	CeO_2; PrO_2

TABLE 32 (Continued)

Compound type	Structure type	Actinide compounds	IVa, Va, VIa compounds	Lanthanide compounds
Oxides, sulfides, selenides and tellurides	γNb_2O_5	γU_2O_5; Pa_2O_5; αU_3O_8	γNb_2O_5; Ta_2O_5	
	Th_3P_4	$Pu_2S_3 - Pu_3S_4$		$Ce_2S_3 - Ce_3S_4$
Nitrides, phosphides, arsenides, etc.	NaCl	ThN; UN; PuN; NpN; $ThP_{0.75}$; UP; PuP; ThAs; UAs; PuAs; USb; UBi; PuBi	ZrN; $\gamma VN_{0.7 \to 1.0}$; NbN; γCrN; WN; $Ti_{0.42 \to 1.16}N$	LaN; CeN; PrN; NdN; GdN; LaP; CeP; PrP; NdP; LaAs; CeAs; PrAs; NdAs; LaSb; LaBi; CeBi; CeSb; PrSb; PrBi
Carbides, silicides, etc.	NaCl	ThC; UC; PuC; NpC	TiC; VC	
	CaC_2	UC_2		LaC_2; CeC_2; PrC_2; NdC_2; SmC_2
	FeB	USi; PuSi	ZrSi	
	$\alpha ThSi_2$	$\alpha ThSi_2$; αUSi_2; $\alpha PuSi_2$; $NpSi_2$; $PuGe_2$		$LaSi_2$; $CeSi_2$; $PrSi_2$; $NdSi_2$; $SmSi_2$; $PrGe_2$
	$CaPb_3$	USi_3; UGe_3; USn_3; UPb_3; $ThPb_3$; $PuGe_3$; $PuSn_3$; $PuPb_3$		$CePb_3$; $CeSn_3$; $LaPb_3$; $LaSn_3$; $PrPb_3$; $PrSn_3$

TABLE 32 (Continued)

Compound type	Structure type	Actinide compounds	IVa, Va, VIa compounds	Lanthanide compounds
Borides, aluminides, etc.	AlB_2	UB_2; UGa_2; $ThAl_2$	ZrB_2; NbB_2; TaB_2; MoB_2; TiB_2; VB_2; CrB_2	$LaGa_2$; $CeGa_2$; $PrGa_2$
	UB_4	ThB_4; UB_4		CeB_4
	CaB_6	ThB_6		LaB_6; CeB_6; NdB_6 etc.
	$MgCu_2$	UAl_2; $PuAl_2$; $NpAl_2$		$CeAl_2$; $LaAl_2$
	$BaAl_4$	UAl_4		$LaAl_4$; $CeAl_4$
Intermetallides of IIb and Ib subgroups	$NaZn_{13}$	$ThBe_{13}$; UBe_{13}; $PuBe_{13}$; $NpBe_{13}$	$ZrBe_{13}$	$CeBe_{13}$
	AlB_2	$ThZn_2$; UHg_2	$ZrBe_2$	
		Phase separation in system U—Ag	Phase separation in systems W—Ag; Cr—Ag	
Intermetallides of VIIa and VIII subgroups	$ThMn_{12}$	$ThMn_{12}$	$CrBe_{12}$; VBe_{12}; $NbBe_{12}$; $MoBe_{12}$	
	$MgZn_2$	$ThMn_2$; $PuOs_2$; UNi_2	WFe_2; $TiFe_2$; $TiMn_2$; $ZrMn_2$; $ZrRe_2$; $ZrOs_2$; $TaMn_2$; $TaFe_2$; $NbMn_2$	
	$MgCu_2$	UMn_2; $PuMn_2$; $PuFe_2$; UFe_2; UOs_2; $PuCo_2$; UCo_2; $PuNi_2$; UIr_2	$\alpha TiCo_2$; $ZrFe_2$; $ZrCo_2$; $NbCo_2$; $TaCo_2$	$CeCo_2$; $CeNi_2$; $LaNi_2$; $PrNi_2$; $CeFe_2$; $CePt_2$

134

TABLE 32 (Continued)

Compound type	Structure type	Actinide compounds	IVa, Va, VIa compounds	Lanthanide compounds
Intermetallides of VIIa and VIII subgroups	CaZn$_5$	ThFe$_5$; ThCo$_5$; ThNi$_5$; PuNi$_5$		LaNi$_5$; CeCo$_5$; CeNi$_5$; P,Ni$_5$
Systems with elements of subgroups IVa, Va, VIa	αF	*Continuous series of solid solutions*		
		γU–βTi; γU–βZr; γU–Nb; γU–40at.%Mo; βTh–βZr; βTh–βHf	βTi–V; βTi–Mo; βTi–Nb; Mo–W; Mo–Cr; W–Ta; Nb–Ta; Nb–Mo; Nb–W; Ta–Mo	
		Eutectic and peritectic systems		
		Th–Ti; Th–Nb; U–V; Pu–V; U–Ta; Th–Cr; U–Cr; Pu–Cr; Th–W; U–W		
		U$_2$Ti; δ(U–Zr); γ(U–Mo)	*Ordered phases*	
	βU	βU	*Analogy with βU* σ(Cr–Fe); (V–Ni) σ(Cr–Mn); (V–Mn) σ(V–Fe); (V–Co) σ(Mo–Re); (W–Re) σ(V–Ni); (Cr–Co)	

summary is far from complete, as many chemical systems and compounds which might be considered have not been discovered, investigated, or studied from the crystal-chemical aspect. This is especially true of the lanthanides, although the chemistry of the transition IVa, Va, and VIa elements and the actinides is also far from complete. It is to be expected that as experimental data accumulate Table 32 will be amplified by new examples illustrating further crystal-chemical resemblance between the compounds of actinides, lanthanides, and the IVa, Va, and VIa elements.

It is clear from Table 32 that quadrivalent *halides* — the fluorides of thorium, uranium, neptunium, and plutonium—are isostructural among themselves and also isostructural both with the IVa, Va, VIa compounds (ZrF_4, HfF_4) and with the lanthanide compound CeF_4. All these compounds have monoclinic structure of the ZrF_4 type [67], with very similar values for the lattice constants and the angle β, and the same atomic parameters; this shows similarity of the chemical bonding in tetrafluorides of the actinides, lanthanides, and the IVa, Va, and VIa elements.

Table 32 shows that the trivalent *halides* of the actinide and lanthanide elements crystallizing in the LaF_3 or UCl_3 structural types are completely isostructural. The trivalent halides of the IVa, Va, and VIa elements have been studied very little as yet.

In the *hydride* group there is complete crystal-chemical analogy between the dihydrides (or dideuterides) of thorium and zirconium, which have the same ThD_2 type of structure, considered earlier (see p. 102). Because of the scarcity of experimental data on hydrides in general and on hydrides of the lanthanide elements in particular, no further comparisons can be made.

In the group of *oxides, sulfides, selenides,* and *tellurides,* Table 32 shows further examples of the crystal-chemical analogy between compounds of the actinide, lanthanide, and IVa, Va, and VIa elements, although here again lack of adequate data, especially on the sesquioxides and sulfides of the IVa, Va, and VIa elements, prevents complete comparison.

The quadrivalent oxides ThO_2, UO_2, ZrO_2 and CeO_2, which have structure of the fluorite type, are not only isostructural but isomorphous with each other, as they form continuous series or very wide regions of solid solutions [103]. This fact provides conclusive crystal-chemical evidence for the great chemical similarity of these oxides of thorium, uranium, zirconium, and cerium.

The fact that the highest "quinquevalent" oxides of uranium and protactinium are isostructural with the corresponding oxides of niobium and tantalum [1, 100] is especially significant in this group of compounds. The lanthanides apparently do not form analogous oxides, as their valence does not exceed +4.

In their highest oxides uranium and the transuranium elements are sexivalent and possibly octavalent (only hydroxides corresponding to the octavalent state are known at present), but the crystal chemistry of these oxides has not been studied. At least four crystalline modifications of UO_3 are known—α, β, γ, and δ—but the atomic configuration has been determined only for UO_3 (see p. 101). However, $\alpha\, UO_3$ was found not to be isostructural with any of the known trioxides of the metals of the IVa, Va, and VIa subgroups. The chemistry of the higher oxides of the actinide and the IVa, Va, and VIa elements is very complex and has been studied hardly at all as yet. It is to be expected that when the crystal structure of β, γ, and $\delta\, UO_3$ has been determined and the polymorphism and chemical composition of the higher oxides of metals in the IVa, Va, and VIa subgroups have been studied in detail, further examples will be found of the crystal-chemical "isostructural analogy" between the actinides and the IVa, Va, and VIa elements.

Nevertheless, although examples of "isostructural analogy" are lacking at present, there is a quite definite "stoichiometric analogy" between the higher oxides of the actinide and the IVa, Va, and VIa elements, but not of the lanthanide elements. By analogy with UO_3 there are the oxides WO_3, MoO_3, CrO_3, whereas lanthanides do not form trioxides.

The *nitride, carbide,* and *boride* groups reveal further isostructural analogies between actinide compounds on the one hand,

and compounds of the lanthanides and of the IVa, Va, and VIa elements on the other. In these groups the analogy between the actinides and lanthanides is more prominent than that between actinides and compounds of the IVa, Va, and VIa elements.

Superposition of homopolar (covalent) and metallic bonding in the compounds with decreasing number of the subgroup of the periodic system leads to progressive decrease of the role of ionic bonding between unlike atoms and to increased obscurity of the "normal" valences of the atoms in compounds. This effect becomes most prominent in intermetallic compounds or *intermetallides*, where the effective valences of the metals are still unknown in most cases.

However, this does not prevent us from drawing further crystal-chemical parallels between compounds of actinides, lanthanides, and elements of the IVa, Va, and VIa compounds in the intermetallide groups, which contain some very convincing examples of the similarity between actinides and the IVa, Va, and VIa metals. When the valences of atoms in metals and intermetallides have been interpreted quantitatively, the causes of the "dual similarity" of the actinides to the lanthanides and to the IVa, Va, and VIa elements will become clear; the qualitative nature of this similarity leaves no doubts even at the present time.

It is clear from Table 32 that the intermetallides crystallizing in the AlB_2, $NaZn_{13}$, $ThMn_{12}$, $MgZn_2$, $MgCu_2$ and $CaZn_5$ structural types include representatives of actinide compounds, compounds of the IVa, Va, and VIa elements, and lanthanide compounds. Therefore in this respect the intermetallides provide a continuation of the "isostructural analogies" established above for the compounds of these elements with nonmetals and semimetals.

Another type of analogy, by the nature of the interaction, can be appropriately introduced here. Such physicochemical effects as phase separation, i.e., immiscibility of metals in the liquid, fused state are significant, in addition to the formation of isostructural compounds, in establishing chemical resemblances between particular elements. The phase separation in the system $U - Ag$ is probably attributable to the same chemical causes, still obscure, as those responsible for phase separation in systems containing silver and IVa elements, namely, W — Ag and Cr — Ag [101].

The most convincing evidence for the similarity between the actinide elements, and particularly thorium and uranium, and the IVa, Va, and VIa elements is the formation of continuous or extensive series of isomorphous solid solutions of βTh and γU with the cubic body-centered metals of subgroups IVa, Va, and VIa; namely, with βTi, βZr, βHf, Nb and Mo. Examples are given in Table 32, which also contains systems with unlimited solubility in the solid state between the IVa, Va, and VIa elements themselves.

This type of isomorphism is not found in "actinide — lanthanide" systems where, as Table 7 shows, phase separation occurs in the liquid state, with immiscibility in the solid state.

Table 32 shows that continuous series of *liquid* molten solutions, forming eutectic or peritectic mixtures on cooling, have been found in the systems: thorium — titanium, thorium — vanadium, thorium — chromium, thorium — niobium, thorium — tungsten, uranium — vanadium, uranium — tantalum, uranium — chromium, uranium — tungsten, plutonium — vanadium, plutonium — chromium, and uranium — molybdenum. These systems also often form considerable regions of limited solid solutions of metals of the IVa, Va, and VIa subgroups; mainly in γU and β Th, and considerably less in αU, βU, and αTh. For example, U dissolves about 10 atomic % of vanadium or over 40 atomic % of molybdenum [20, 62].

Prolonged low-temperature annealing of solid solutions of IVa, Va, and VIa elements in uranium sometimes results in transition from a disordered to an ordered atomic arrangement, with the formation of the so-called "ordered phases." Table 32 contains three firmly established examples of ordered phases, namely: U_2Ti; δ (U — Zr) and γ' (U — Mo). Although the data discussed earlier (see p. 49—50) on the crystal structure of these phases are not final, they are conclusive evidence of their "ordered" nature. In all three cases ordering of the atoms in the crystal lattice is accompanied by a change of symmetry.

Analogous "order ⇌ disorder" transitions are known to take place in many systems of related metals forming continuous or very extensive regions of solid solutions, such as gold—copper, gold-platinum, iron—chromium, etc.

It has already been pointed out (see p. 47) that formation of continuous regions of solid solutions and the processes of atomic ordering which take place in these solid solutions at low temperatures are characteristic of elements of the same subgroup of the periodic systems, or elements which are very closely related chemically. It is clear from Table 32 that IVa, Va, and VIa elements have a great tendency to form continuous series of solid solutions with one another as well as with γ-uranium and β-thorium.

All these "isomorphous analogies" provide new and further crystal-chemical and physicochemical confirmation of the close chemical relationship of the actinide elements, and especially of thorium and uranium, to the IVa, Va, and VIa elements.

A very interesting crystal-chemical fact, which is also indicative of the chemical similarity between the actinides and the IVa, Va, and VIa elements is that β-uranium is isostructural with the α phases [102] of systems in which one *obligatory* component is a IVa, Va, or VIa element and the other an element from group VIII of the periodic system. Examples of such phases are given in Table 32.

All the above facts demonstrate the undoubted, even if still inadequately explained, chemical resemblance between the actinide and the IVa, Va, and VIa elements, which cannot be disregarded.

The similarity between the actinides and the lanthanides is unquestionable, and is now effectively explained.

All this is indicative of the duality of the chemical nature of the actinide elements, which resemble the lanthanides and the IVa, Va, and VIa elements simultaneously, and it also demonstrates the inadequacy of the term "actinides" for the transactinium elements.

LITERATURE CITED

1. W. H. Zachariasen, "Crystal chemistry of the 5f elements," The Actinide Elements, edited by G. T. Seaborg and J. J. Katz [Russian translation] (Moscow, IL, 1955) pp. 623–646. [Mc Graw-Hill]
2. P. Chiotti, J. Electrochem. Soc. 101, No. 11, 567 (1954).
3. F. G. Foote, Physical Metallurgy of Uranium, (Intern. Conf. on the Peaceful Uses of Atomic Energy, Rep. No. 555, USA, Geneva, 1955).
4. C. W. Jacob and B. E. Warren, J. Amer. Chem. Soc. 59, 2588 (1937).
5. J. S. Lukesh, Acta cryst. 2, No. 6, 420 (1949).
6. L. Pauling, J. Amer. Chem. Soc. 69, 542 (1947).
7. C. W. Tucker, Acta cryst. 4, 425 (1951); 5, 395 (1952).
8. J. Thewlis, Acta cryst. 5, 790 (1952).
9. C. W. Tucker and P. Senio, Acta cryst. 6, 753 (1953); 7, No. 11, 752 (1954).
10. J. Thewlis and H. Steeple, Acta cryst. 7, No. 4, 323 (1954).
10a. C. W. Tucker, P. Senio, J. Thewlis and H. Steeple, Acta cryst. 9, No. 4 (1956).
11. International-Tabellen zur Bestimmung von Kristallstrukturen, Erster Band (Berlin, 1935).
12. McLennan and McKay, Trans. Roy. Soc. Canada (3), 24, 1 (1930).
13. A. S. Wilson and R. E. Rundle, Acta cryst. 2, No. 2, 126 (1949).
14. J. Thewlis, Nature 168, 198 (1951).
15. W. H. Zachariasen, Acta cryst. 5, No. 5, 660 (1952).
16. E. S. Makarov, Proc. Acad. Sci. USSR 59, No. 5 (1948).
17. E. R. Jette, J. Chem. Phys. 23, No. 2, 365 (1955).
18. W. H. Zachariasen and F. H. Ellinger, Acta cryst. 8, No. 7, 431 (1955).
19. O. N. Carlson, P. Chiotti, G. Murphy et. al., The Metallurgy of Thorium and its Alloys (Intern. Conf. on the Peaceful Uses of Atomic Energy. Rep. No. 556, U.S.A., Geneva, 1955).
20. H. A. Saller and F. A. Rough, The Alloys of Uranium (Ibid., Rep. No. 558, U. S. A.).
21. A. S. Coffinberry and F. H. Ellinger, Ibid. (Rep. No. 826, U. S. A.).
22. A. G. Knapton, Acta cryst. 7, No. 5, 457 (1954); M. C. Udy and F. W. Boulger, J. of Metals 6, No. 2, (Sect. 2), 207 (1954).
23. H. A. Saller, "Uranium and its alloys," Reactor Handbook: Materials and General Properties. (United States Atomic Energy Comiss., McGraw-Hill Book Co., 1955), pp. 383–436.

24. M. H. Mueller, Acta cryst. 8, No. 12, 849 (1955).
25. C. W. Tucker, J. Inst. of Metals 78, 760 (1950–1951).
26. J. V. Florio, R. E. Rundle and A. I. Snow, Acta cryst. 5, No. 4, 449 (1952).
27. N. C. Baenziger, R. E. Rundle, A. I. Snow and A. S. Wilson, Acta cryst. 3, 34 (1950).
28. J. V. Florio, N. C. Baenziger and R. E. Rundle, Acta cryst. 9, No. 4, 367 (1956).
29. T. J. Heal and G. I. Williams, Acta cryst. 8, No. 8, 494 (1955).
30. J. R. Murray, J. Inst. of Metals 84, 91 (1955–1956).
31. J. D. Grogan, R. J. Pleasance and B. E. Williams, J. Inst. of Metals 82, 141–147 (1953–1954).
32. R. W. Buzzard and J. J. Park, J. Research Nation. Bur. Stand. 53, No. 5, 291 (1954).
33. W. C. Koehler, J. Singer and A. S. Coffinberry, Acta cryst. 5, No. 3, 394 (1952).
34. O. J. C. Runnalls, Acta cryst. 7, No. 2, 222 (1954).
35. E. S. Makarov and L. S. Gudkov, Crystallography 1, No. 6, 650 (1956).
36. E. S. Makarov and S. I. Vinogradov, Crystallography 1, No. 6, 634 (1956).
37. R. E. Rundle and A. S. Wilson, Acta cryst. 2, 148 (1949).
38. A. Zalkin and D. H. Templeton, Acta cryst. 6, No. 3, 269 (1953).
39. R. Kiessling, Acta Chem. Scand. 4, 209 (1950).
40. J. Meyer and F. Kasper, Z. anorg. allg. Chem. 155, 49 (1926).
41. P. B. Braun and J. H. N. van Vucht, Acta cryst. 8, No. 2, 117 (1955); No. 4, 246 (1955); A. F. Anderson and J. A. Goedkoop, Ibid., 118; J. R. Murray, J. Inst. of Metal 84, 91 (1955–1956).
42. P. Gordon and A. K. Kaufman, J. of Metals 188, 182 (1950).
43. B. R. T. Frost and J. T. Maskrey, J. Inst. of Metals 82, No. 4, 171 (1953).
44. B. S. Borie, Trans. Amer. Inst. Mining Eng. 191, 800 (1951).
45. O. J. C. Runnalls, J. of Metals 5, No. 11, 1460 (1953).
46. E. S. Makarov and V. A. Levdik, Crystallography 1, No. 6, 644 (1956).
47. S. T. Konobeevskii, "Phase diagrams of certain systems based on plutonium," Proceedings of Session of the Academy of Sciences USSR on the Peaceful Use of Atomic Energy, June 1–5, 1955, Div. Chem. Sci. [In Russian] (Moscow, Izd. AN SSSR, 1955) pp. 362–376.
48. G. Brauer and Mitius, Z. anorg. allg. Chem. 249, 325 (1942).
49. O. J. C. Runnalls and R. R. Boucher, Acta cryst. 8, No. 10, 592 (1955).
50. R. Ferro, Acta cryst. 8, No. 6, 360 (1955).
51. J. J. Katz and E. Rabinowitch, The Chemistry of Uranium [Russian translation] (Moscow, IL, 1954).
52. A. Jandelli, Atti Accad. Naz. Lincei, Rend. Cl. sci. fis., mat. e nat. 13, 138 (1953).

53. R. Ferro, C. A., 47, No. 14, 6729; No. 20, 10307; No. 21, 10981, 11114 (1953).
54. R. W. M. D'Eye, J. Chem. Soc., 1670—72 (1953); 2555—62 (1952).
55. R. Ferro, Z. anorg. allg. Chem. 275, No. 6, 320 (1954).
56. R. W. M. D'Eye and P. G. Sellman, J. Chem. Soc., 3760—66 (1954).
57. G. T. Seaborg, "Correlation of properties as actinide transition series," The Actinide Elements (edited by G. T. Seaborg and J. J. Katz) [Russian translation] (Moscow, IL, 1955) pp. 594—622.
58. M. C. Udy and F. W. Boulger, J. of Metals 6, No. 2 (Sect. 2), 207 (1954).
59. R. C. Evans, Introduction to Crystal Chemistry [Russian translation, translated and augmented by E. S. Makarov] (Moscow, Goskhimizdat, 1948).
60. O. J. C. Runnalls, Canad. J. Chem. 34, No. 2, 133 (1956).
61. E. S. Makarov, a) additions to Russian translation of R. C. Evans, Introduction to Crystal Chemistry (Moscow, Goskhimizdat, 1948); b) Studies in Crystal Chemistry of Compounds of Variable Composition (Dissertation) [In Russian] (N. S. Kurnakov Inst. General and Inorganic Chemistry, Acad. Sci. USSR, Moscow, 1953) 24, pp. 284—419; Summary, p. 16.
62. H. A. Saller and F. A. Rough, A Compilation of U. S. A. and U. Kingdom Uranium and Thorium Constitutional Diagrams. (Battelle Memorial Inst., Columbus, Ohio (1954)); U. S. Atomic Energy Comm., B. M. J.—1000, 141 (1955).
63. F. Bertaut and P. Blum, Compt. rend. 229, 666 (1949).
64. W. H. Zachariasen, Acta cryst. 2, No. 2, 94 (1949).
65. W. H. Zachariasen, Acta cryst. 5, No. 1, 17 (1952).
66. E. B. Hunt and R. E. Rundle, J. Amer. Chem. Soc. 73, 4777 (1951).
67. W. H. Zachariasen, Acta cryst. 2, No. 6, 388 (1949).
68. W. H. Zachariasen, J. Chem. Phys. 16, No. 3, 254 (1948).
69. W. H. Zachariasen, Acta cryst. 1, No. 5, 265 (1948).
70. R. C. L. Mooney, Acta cryst. 2, 189 (1949).
71. R. W. M. D'Eye, J. Chem. Soc., 2764 (1950).
72. W. H. Zachariasen, Acta cryst. 2, No. 6, 390 (1949).
73. W. H. Zachariasen, Acta cryst. 2, No. 1, 296 (1949).
74. D. T. Peterson, P. F. Diljak and C. L. Vold, Acta cryst. 9, No. 12, 1036 (1956).
75. W. H. Zachariasen, Acta cryst. 1, No. 6, 285 (1948).
76. H. R. Hoekstra and S. Siegel, Intern. Conf. on the Peaceful Uses of Atomic Energy. Rep. No. 737, U. S. A., Geneva, 1955.
77. W. H. Zachariasen, Acta cryst. 2, No. 5, 288 (1949).
78. W. H. Zachariasen, Acta cryst. 2, No. 5, 291 (1949).
79. M. Picon and J. Flahaut, Compt. rend., 237, No. 19, 1160 (1953); 240, No. 22, 2150 (1955).
80. W. H. Zachariasen, Acta cryst. 2, No. 1, 57 (1949).
81. R. E. Rundle, N. C. Baenziger, A. S. Wilson and R. A. McDonald, J. Amer. Chem. Soc. 70, 99 (1948).

82. Strukturbericht, v. I–VII. (1931–1943). Strukturbericht, v. IX–XII (1956). (Becker und Erler, Leipzig).
83. M. Zumbusch, Z. anorg. allg. Chem. 245, 402 (1941).
84. A. Jandelli, Atti. Accad. Naz. Lincei, Rend. Cl. sci. fis., mat. e nat., 13, 138 (1953).
85. R. E. Rundle, C. G. Shull and E. O. Woolan, Acta cryst. 5, No. 1, 22 (1952).
86. W. H. Zachariasen, Acta cryst. 6, No. 5, 393 (1953).
87. R. N. R. Mulford, F. H. Ellinger and W. H. Zachariasen, J. Amer. Chem. Soc. 76, No. 1, 297 (1954).
88. R. E. Rundle, J. Amer. Chem. Soc. 73, No. 9, 4172 (1951).
89. R. N. R. Mulford and G. E. Sturdy, J. Amer. Chem. Soc. 77, No. 13, 3449 (1955).
90. G. Hagg and N. Schonberg, Acta cryst. 7, 251 (1954).
91. L. Pauling, The Nature of the Chemical Bond (Cornell Univ. Press, Ithaca, N. Y., 1939).
92. N. Bohr, Die Seltenen Erden von Standpunkte des Atombaues (by G. Hevesy) (Springer, Berlin, 1927).
93. V. M. Goldschmidt, "Geochemische Verteilungsgesetze der Elemente, V." Skrif. Norske Vidensk. Akad. Oslo, J. mat.-nat. K1., No. 7 (1925).
94. N. Bohr, Nature 112, 30 (1923).
95. V. M. Goldschmidt, "Geochemische Verteilungesetze der Elemente, V." Skrif. Norske Vidensk. Akad., Oslo, mat.-nat. K1., No. 2 (1926); Trav. Congr. jubilaire Mendeleev 2, 387 (1937).
96. N. Bohr, Theory of Spectra and Atomic Constitution (2nd ed.) (Cambr. Univ. Press, N. Y., 1924) p. 112.
97. E. M. McMillan and P. H. Abelson, Phys. Rev. 57, 1185 (1940).
98. G. T. Seaborg and A. C. Wahl, J. Amer. Chem. Soc. 70, 1128 (1948).
99. G. T. Seaborg, "Correlation of properties as actinide transition series," The Actinide Elements (edited by G. T. Seaborg and J. J. Katz) [Russian translation] (Moscow, IL, 1955).
100. W. T. Holser, Acta cryst. 9, No. 2, 196 (1956).
101. R. Ferro, Gazz. chim. ital. 85, No. 7–8, 888 (1955).
102. D. P. Shoemaker and G. B. Bergman, J. Amer. Chem. Soc. 72, No. 12, 5793 (1950); G. J. Dickins, A. M. B. Douglas and W. H. Taylor, Nature 167, No. 4240, 192 (1951). G. B. Bergman and D. P. Shoemaker, Acta cryst. 7, No. 857 (1954); W. B. Pearson and J. W. Christian, Acta cryst. 5, 157 (1952).
103. H. R. Hoekstra and S. Siegel, Intern. Conf. on the Peaceful Uses of Atomic Energy, Rep. No. 737, U. S. A., Geneva, 1955.
104. A. F. Kapustinskii, Crystallography 1, No. 4, 382 (1956).
105. W. H. Zachariasen and F. Ellinger, Acta cryst. 10, No. 12, 776 (1957).
106. H. M. Finniston and J. P. Howe, Metallurgy and Fuels, v. I, Ser. V. Progress in Nuclear Energy, Pergamon Press Ltd., London (1956) pp. 373–374.

107. H. M. Finniston and J. P. Howe, Metallurgy and Fuels, v. I, Ser. V. Progress in Nuclear Energy, Pergamon Press Ltd., London (1956) p. 389.
108. H. M. Finniston and J. P. Howe, Metallurgy and Fuels, v. I, Ser. V. Progress in Nuclear Energy, Pergamon Press Ltd., London (1956) pp. 390—396.
109. E. K. Halteman, Acta cryst. 10, No. 3, 166 (1957).
110. E. Wait, J. Inorg. and Nuclear Chem. 1, No. 4—5, 309 (1955).
111. R. J. Teitel, J. of Metals 9, No. 1 (Sect. 2), 131 (1957).
112. W. H. Zachariasen, J. Amer. Chem. Soc. 76, No. 23, 5937 (1954).
113. P. Graf, B. B. Cunningham, C. H. Dauben, J. C. Wallman, D. H. Templeton and H. Ruben, J. Amer. Chem. Soc. 78, No. 10, 2340 (1956).
114. A. N. Holden and W. E. Seymour, J. of Metals 8, No. 10 (Sect. 2), 1312 (1956).
115. J. M. Silcock, J. of Metals 9, No. 4 (Sect. 2), 521 (1957).
116. E. S. Makarov, Crystallography 3 (1958).
117. A. C. Larson, D. T. Cromer and C. K. Stambaugh, Acta cryst. 10, No. 7, 443 (1957).

6-23-66